UNIVERSITY OF KNOWLEDGE

GLENN FRANK, B.A., M.A , LITT.D., L.H.D., LL.D., *Editor-in-Chief*

PRINTED AND BOUND IN THE UNITED STATES
OF AMERICA BY THE CUNEO PRESS, INC.

Every Branch of Knowledge Man Possesses May Be Applied To Some Good Purpose

Courtesy John A. Maloney. From the portrait by Ellis M. Silvette

EDISON

"HE CAPTURED LIGHT AND CAGED IT IN A GLASS,
THEN HARNESSED IT FOREVER TO A WIRE;
HE GAVE MEN ROBOTS WITH NO BACKS TO TIRE
IN BEARING BURDENS FOR THE TOILING MASS."

—GEORGE SANFORD HOLMES

UNIVERSITY OF KNOWLEDGE

GLENN FRANK, EDITOR-IN-CHIEF

GREAT INVENTORS

AND

THEIR INVENTIONS

BY

JOHN A. MALONEY, B.A.

Assistant to the Director
Museum of Science and Industry
Chicago

AND

ASSOCIATES

•

UNIVERSITY OF KNOWLEDGE, INCORPORATED

CHICAGO

INTRODUCTION

This is a book about the great inventors and their inventions. In so far as it tells of the inventors and how they went at their enterprise of invention, this book does for the reader what a preceding volume of brief biographies does. It enables the reader to shadow genius at work, and, as I said in my introduction to the volume of biographies, if it be true that, in the main, we learn by doing, then the next best thing is to watch how the great spirits of all time have done things.

The great inventors have been the greater surprisers. Again and again they have shamed our limited outlook. They have done the things we have said could not be done. They have been experts in the impossible.

The inventor is not the bought-and-paid-for slave of business and industry. He is blood brother of the scientist and the artist. He is animated by the itch to invent as the scientist is animated by the itch to know and the artist by the itch to create. The inventor does not sit with folded hands until some human need comes to him, like a cry out of the night, or some business need is put to him, as a call from the counting house, and then set feverishly at work to invent a new gadget or machine to meet the need. He marches steadily alongside the scientist into the territory of the unknown, checking and verifying the scientist's hunches and generalizations with instruments that test their truth.

The inventor has so often done the impossible and disproved our doubts that recent years have seen the rise of a new faith in the inventor as a door to what may seem beyond the range of the possible. This is a new phase in the development of our attitude towards inventors and invention.

A long run of years ago, a clerk in the United States Patent Office resigned his post with the explanation, "I want to be on the safe side. Nearly all the inventions that are possible have been invented. Soon there will be no more, and this office will have to close. I want to get into something else now while I have the opportunity."

Andrew Carnegie was convinced that, in 1905, the automobile had about reached the perfection of its development. "We are greatly pleased with our new Winton," he wrote. "From the very start it has done its work and never failed us. There may be improvements yet to come in such autos, but it is difficult to see much room for them."

R. E. Olds, among the pioneer designers of automobiles, wrote in an advertisement in the *Scientific American* of January 6, 1912, "The car I now bring out is considered by me as pretty close to finality—so close that I call it 'my farewell car.' I shall let it stand as my topmost achievement."

We still hear such statements in the field of *social invention*, but we would have to search far for any such assertions of limits to the capacity of men in the field of *physical invention*. We have come to believe that man can do about anything he puts his mind to in the field of physical invention.

This is a definite gain. This popular faith in science and invention has been a sustaining factor in the morale of our army of scientists and inventors. It rings as a kind of call to arms through our laboratories.

But, alongside this growing popular confidence that scientists and inventors can do about anything they set out to do by way of solving problems and inventing instruments, there has lately arisen a mood of skepticism about the social effect of all that the scientists and inventors have been doing.

Reformers arise who would put a ring in the nose of invention and call a halt on scientific research. Why go on inventing new machines, they say, if machinery throws men out of work and gives us a baffling problem which the professors call technological unemployment? Are the inventors and engineers, after all, the social benefactors they have been said to be?

I think they are. It is not the fault of the scientists and inventors if we are shortsighted in our use of the results of their labors. Walter Polakov was right, I think, when he said that our trouble is not technological unemployment as much as the unemployment of technology. Our way out does not lie in slowing the inventors down to the pace of our politicians, but in seeing to it that social invention keeps step with physical invention.

And, then, I am not sure that the inventors and scientists and engineers show up so badly alongside the reformers if we test them solely by what their work has meant to the mine-run of human beings.

Some years ago Count Richard Nicholas Coudenhove-Kalergi wrote a little book which, as far as I know, has not been translated into English. It was called *Apologie der Technik*. In it, he argued that the true champions of the masses are the engineers and inventors rather than the social reformers. The real emancipations of the last century and a half, he insisted, have been the unconscious by-products of technical advance rather than the conscious achievements of social reform. Societies for the prevention of cruelty to animals had done much to improve the lot of the horse, but it remained for the inventor of the automobile really to emancipate the horse from undue drudgery and unnecessary suffering. The galley slaves of older days were freed not by hot headed abolitionists but by the cool headed inventor of the marine engine. Social legislation had done much to make the life of seamen more livable, but the use of fuel oil was the real force that emancipated them from the inferno of the stoke-hole.

The final goal of inventor and engineer is to make available to the masses comforts and conveniences that now only the wealthy may have. In other words, whether we realize it or not, the inventors and the engineers are waging a war of human liberation. And it may be, as Kalergi insists, that their way of fighting this war of human liberation is a better way than many reformers have adopted. The social reformer fights wealth. The inventor fights want. The social reformer fights slave drivers. The inventor fights slavery.

In a way, it is beside the point for me to throw all this general problem into an introduction to this book of inventors and their inventions. The supreme value of this book, I am sure, will lie in its giving the reader the chance to watch a brilliant gallery of marvelous minds at work.

We cannot so much as walk around the block, ride to our work, get through the day's routine, eat a meal, phone to a neighbor, or switch out the light by our bedside without encountering the wide world of invention. Our lives are largely colored and controlled by the fruits of invention. Life will be more meaningful for us if we knew something about the men and methods back of all these inventions. We may get some enjoyment from listening to a great symphony even if we know nothing about composer, musicians, or instruments. But we never really enjoy great music without some insight into the purposes of the composer and the nature of the instruments through which his spirit wings its way to ours.

Invention came that men might have life and that they might have it more abundantly. We owe it to ourselves to understand the devoted minds that stand back of the great inventions.

GLENN FRANK, Editor-in-chief.

PREFACE

In the selection of material for this volume on the subject of inventions, it was necessary for the authors to come to some agreement beforehand, not only as to what method of treatment of the inventions chosen should be used, but also to determine just what we mean by an invention. In other words, when can a device be called a real invention? Every schoolboy knows that Hero of Alexandria, in 120 B.C., constructed an aeolipile, or primitive reaction steam turbine. Can we, therefore, state that Hero is the inventor of the steam engine and therefore responsible for the industrial revolution which the steam engine was to bring about 1900 years later? Obviously not. Hero's device was nothing more or less than an ingenious toy and played no part in the future development of the steam engine. The inventions of Newcomen, Savery and Watt, on the other hand, not only became commercially successful machines but had a profound and lasting effect upon society. Hence, the authors have chosen only those inventions which were successful in the commercial world as we know it, and have credited as the inventors those men who actually brought the device to fruition. If, as some would have it, we were to credit the dreamers who first thought of or sketched inventions, but never succeeded in making them available to mankind, such men as Leonardo da Vinci and perhaps many another before him would have the credit for airplanes, steam engines, and a myriad of other devices.

It will be seen later that few if any modern inventions are purely original in the sense that they spring materially and formally from some fertile brain. The exceptions to this rule are such primitive things as the wheel, the sail, the use of fire, and the bow and arrow. The primitive men who devised these basic inventions were innovators of the first order. That they obtained their first hazy ideas of such inventions from nature is probably true. A stone rolling down a hill may have suggested the wheel;

the rubbing of the limbs of a tree together probably showed the caveman that he could imitate the lightning flash and produce fire; and the spring of a bent sapling may have started the train of thought that led to the construction of the first bow and arrow. On these things we can but speculate, but of the ingenuity of the men who first adapted them there can be no doubt.

The inventive genius of man has fascinated many of the greatest minds in history. Man's technical achievement was at first very slow but when practically unlimited power was placed at his disposal he began to build an artificial environment about himself with amazing alacrity. And the end of his ability to invent is nowhere in sight. Doubtless he will continue to invent until the earth on which he lives is but a burned-out cinder, whirling aimlessly through space. He already has found that, of the countless materials to be found in, on, and above his spinning globe, all are composed of but ninety-two elements. These are his building blocks and even in this, the twentieth century, the Machine Age, he has learned to use but very few of these ninety-two elements to any marked degree.

The purpose of this volume is to discuss a number of the great fundamental inventions which have had profound social and economic effects upon civilization. In addition to giving a few of the highlights in the life of the inventor, the discussions will include only the period of the invention itself with a brief indication of its further development. Thus in the chapter devoted to the typewriter, to take an example, at random, we will find a story of Sholes, the inventor, and of the machine which he perfected. The typewriter has become a great social agent in putting women into industrial and commercial fields, and so the story of its development into such instruments as the electrically-driven typewriter and the teletypewriter is the story of an industry rather than of an invention as such.

Another point may well be taken here before we begin to delve into the fascinating tales of the great inventions. There are scientific discoveries upon which many later inventions depend. Michael Faraday, for example, has been called the greatest experimenter that ever lived. And without his fundamental discoveries many of our inventions would not have occurred as early as they did. Every electric motor and generator depends for its very existence upon his classical discovery of electrical induction. Scientist that he was, he realized that some day his discoveries would have practical application. Gladstone, seeing one of Faraday's experiments, asked of what possible use it could be. "Why, Mr. Prime Minister," answered Faraday, "You will soon be able to tax it!" Benjamin Franklin, when asked a similar question by an elderly lady replied, "Madam, of what use is a newborn child?" The part that pure science plays in the field of invention holds a story as romantic and engrossing as the story of inventions itself.

Chicago   John A. Maloney

January 10, 1938

The following persons have assisted with their research and contributions in the preparation of this volume: J. K. Alexander, Fritz Leiber, Jr., Donald Morris, David M. Saxe, and Gordon Van Arman.

J. A. M.

ACKNOWLEDGMENT

The history of inventions presents a remarkable panorama of objects of all kinds from the smallest gadgets to the greatest steamboats, and from diving machines to rocket ships.

We have had capable co-operation from the following individuals and firms, and public, scientific, and private institutions:

The Museum of Science and Industry, Chicago
International Harvester Co.
The Baltimore and Ohio Railroad Co.
Allis-Chalmers Manufacturing Co.
General Electric Co.
Westinghouse Air Brake Co.
The Pullman Co.
Dr. Robert H. Goddard
Western Union Telegraph Co.
Illinois Bell Telephone Co.
Carnegie-Illinois Steel Co.
The Chicago Historical Society
Mr. Ed Wilcox of Almer Coe and Co.
Hercules Motors Corporation
The Art Institute of Chicago
The Goodyear Tire and Rubber Co., Inc.
Otis Elevator Co.
Lyon and Healy, Inc.
Monark Silver King, Inc.
Mead Cycle Co.
E. C. Fuller Co.
U. S. Navy Recruiting Bureau
International Business Machines Corporation
Alfred Crossley, Chicago
Holmes Projector Co.
Progress Corporation, New York
L. E. Waterman Co.
Iwan Ries & Co.

J. Bradford Pengelly
Picture Editor

TABLE OF CONTENTS

THE INVENTOR AND SOCIETY

"MAN," SAID CARLYLE, "is a tool-using animal. Feeblest of bipeds! Nevertheless, he can use tools and devise tools; with these the granite mountain melts into light dust before him; seas are his smooth highway; winds and fire his unwearying steeds. Nowhere do you find him without tools. Without tools he is nothing; with tools he is all."

Henry Ward Beecher paid this tribute to the inventor: "A tool is but the extension of a man's hand and a machine is but a complex tool; and he that invents a machine augments the power of man and the well-being of mankind."

Both of these men were speaking of invention as they knew it. In their day technological improvements were usually the work of the lone, heroic type of inventor. The names of such men as Watt, Whitney, Howe, Morse, Edison, and Westinghouse, and the other pioneers of the beginnings of the Machine Age, will live forever. The day of their methods, however, is gone. Today technical and scientific innovations first see light of day as they issue from highly organized research laboratories, where co-operative teams of specialists each play a part in the advancing front. Although there are a round half-dozen individuals who claim to be the inventors of such things as television and other modern devices, the truth of the matter is that no one man can be credited. Pick out any similar development of the past quarter-century and you will find on investigation that it is the brain child of chemists, physicists, engineers, artists, and mechanics—a three-dimensional mosaic, the offspring of a hundred or more researchers. No more do inventions pick out individual brains haphazardly in which to germinate. Today we do not find school teachers such as Eli Whitney, inventing a cotton gin. Nor do we find artists devising ingenious machines, as was the case when Samuel F. B. Morse invented the telegraph or Robert Fulton the steamboat. The monk of today confines his activities to teaching and aiding the sick whereas one

BODLEIAN PORTRAIT OF ROGER BACON

of his early predecessors, Roger Bacon, is credited with the invention of gunpowder. Gatling, who invented the machine gun which bears his name, was a physician. Let no one be discouraged by the fact that invention today has passed almost wholly into the hands of trained technicians. The hero worship of the youngster for the great individualistic pioneers in the field of invention should be encouraged. There is still much to be done, and if some future Edison is to appear to invent new things and prove himself to be the exception in this era of organized research, so much the better. Even men as ingenious as Morse were not slow in approaching others for aid and information which they lacked. Were it not for the aid given him by Professor Joseph Henry, Morse might have failed.

There is, however, one hardy perennial, growing in the fertile garden of invention, to whom we can offer no quarter. Have you guessed of whom we speak? He is that stubborn individual, today's alchemist, searching for the philosopher's stone to turn base metal into gold; he is the modern-day replica of the seekers of the spring whose waters would endow them with immortality—he is the perpetual motion addict. Behind locked doors he works, burning the midnight oil, trying to get a machine that would run forever without any external source of energy. The plain fact that you cannot get something for nothing does not stop such people. Many perpetual motion machines have been patented in the past, both in this country and abroad. A few were out and out fakes, easily detectable by any first-class mechanic, while others were ingenious machines—but not perpetual motion. To protect the public from spending their money for nothing—and many a lifetime's savings have been squandered on these devices—the United States Patent Office now refuses to consider any application for a patent on a perpetual motion machine until the application is accompanied by a *working model* of the machine. It is perhaps needless to point out that no working models have been submitted since this ruling went into effect.

BOON OR MISFORTUNE?

Inventions have been praised as the greatest boons to the human race and damned as the greatest misfortunes of mankind. There are few good books available from the pens of serious thinkers who have justly appraised the machine and its social and economic effects. On the other hand, there are any number of books, articles, and speeches constantly streaming from those who condemn the machine and everything connected with it. We have had and will again have demands that science and technology take a holiday. We have had, under various high-sounding names, organizations whose avowed purpose is to persuade mankind to return to the "horse-and-buggy" era.

Perhaps the most effective attempt ever made to demonstrate that the theories of those who condemn the machine are made of whole cloth is that of Dr. James S. Thomas, President of Clarkson College of Technology. In his discussion of what the machine has done for mankind, Dr. Thomas says in part:

> "What we should all remember is, that there are two types of culture in the world; an idealistic culture about which everybody raves, and a materialistic culture about which nobody raves. The idealistic culture

finds its expression in the so-called 'creative arts.' The materialistic culture is expressed in science, invention, machines, business, and other such practical manipulations as enable us to enjoy food, clothing, and shelter. It also does the obviously prosaic thing of paying for our idealistic culture as any taxpayer or philanthropically inclined gentleman with a little change in his pocket can easily testify. It did this for Socrates, it supported Plato, it maintained Aristotle who had the good sense to marry the richest woman in Greece. (Her money gave him plenty of leisure time to think, and I have not the slightest doubt she gave him plenty to think about, so he became a philosopher.) Likewise Dante spent all his life climbing other men's stairs and eating other men's bread, while Shakespeare wrote his immortal plays on contract.

"This materialistic culture continues to carry on today just as it has always done by supporting our schools, hospitals, art galleries and the rest of cultural institutions. The idealistic culture has always traveled upon the back of the materialistic culture for the simple reason that there is no other way for it to get along. The first savage who discovered the value of a trinket he did not own and started bargaining for it, started civilization. The measure of a nation's culture, its width, its breadth, its duration, and its influence is measured by the ability of the business and commerce of its day to pay the bills and carry on.

" 'In the sweat of thy brow shalt thou earn thy bread' is not so much the statement of a curse as the statement of a principle. It is the principle

Courtesy The Art Institute of Chicago

MEUNIER'S MONUMENT TO LABOR: THE MINE
(Original monument in Louvain.)

that human life, human progress, and human culture are based upon energy, some sort of work that must be done by men, by animals or by machines.

"With primitives, this energy for the most part is translated through human muscle, human effort. A little later animals are domesticated and brought into the picture. In more advanced stages come water power, then steam and now gas and electricity, and later perhaps the exploding atom. The development from human muscle to modern machines is marked by ever increasing leisure and the chief characteristic of leisure is its cultural possibilities. Now man is intelligently tending the machine for work instead of devoting ninety per cent of his waking hours to get the simple necessities of existence as he was formerly forced to do.

"Historical evidence is all on the side of the machine. The wide use of science and invention has given us the most miraculous century and a half that the world ever saw. No civilization on this planet ever accomplished so much in so short a time.

"The great idealistic cultural periods of the past came exactly at the time or immediately upon the heels of the best business years such nations enjoyed. The great Periclean Age in Greece came at a time when Greece was trading with a thousand trading posts in the Mediterranean basin. When she lost her commerce, her philosophers went right out the window. The Golden Age of Roman literature came exactly at a time when Rome's commerce was farthest flung. When her economic system played out, Rome went to ruin and her poets and philosophers became only memories. The Italian Renaissance came exactly at a time when Italian business men in Florence, Genoa, Venice, and other cities learned how to take raw materials, convert them into finished products, ship them out to less gifted people in the arts, and with the profits paid for the artistic achievements of the Renaissance."

PROGRESS IN THE WORLD OF INVENTIONS

Thus it is clear that no amount of saying-so can change the fundamental truth that if we are to have civilization we are bound to make progress in inventive technology. We make progress only as we make changes, and the most important changes we make are those which give us either new products from the mind of the inventor or better products than we formerly had. The argument that new inventions throw men out of work is so patently false that it is astonishing how it persists. Take away the great inventions of the last century and what happens to the millions who are now employed in manufacturing automobiles, radios, and the thousands of other products of the Machine Age?

JAMES WATT
Scottish engineer, who was a leader in
The Industrial Revolution.

They either become slaves to themselves or a master, scratching out a meager existence from the stubborn soil or they die like flies from famine and pestilence. Look to those civilizations which have been most backward in adopting machines, either through lack of raw materials or because of their traditions and there you will find the least culture, the least comfort, and, to a marked degree, slavery in its worst form.

The large cities of the world did not grow by chance. Thriving centers of commerce, dotted with magnificent towers of stone, steel, and cement, owe their existence partly to their natural advantages, but their greatest step forward came as a result of what historians have always called The Industrial Revolution. The leading actor on this particular stage in the drama of civilization was James Watt, a Scottish engineer, instrument maker to the University of Glasgow, and the man who brought the crude steam pump of Newcomen and Savery to comparative perfection.

Imagine yourself back in the days in England when Watt gave the steam engine its greatest forward push by the invention of the separate condenser, and note both the similarity and the dissimilarity of those days to the social change through which we are passing today. Up to that time industry was carried on by craftsmen who depended largely upon their own strength and upon mechanical contrivances which had seen little or no improvement for centuries. An ancient Athenian flour mill, working at top speed, ground about two barrels of flour a day. When Watt was born flour mills had not progressed appreciably and were not much ahead of those in Athens, so far as production was concerned. Iron was fashioned by a blacksmith with an open forge and a cumbersome anvil.

As early as the time of Queen Elizabeth, England faced a fuel crisis. The forests had been hewn down and no thought was given to reforestation. The coal mines at that time were mostly open pits into which water ran and prevented the miners from working. Pumps, worked by horses, were unable to cope with the situation. A great invention was needed to save England from ruin.

There were many engineers in England at that time who needed no incentive to realize the problem that had to be faced sooner or later. But the two successful inventors were two engineers, Newcomen and Savery. They invented a steam pump which took the surplus water from the mines at a faster rate than horses could do it. This they left as a technical heritage and the heir to it was James Watt. The crude and wasteful steam pump of Newcomen and Savery needed the genius of Watt to bring it to a point where it could be used by other industries. Yet even Watt did not foresee the possibilities of his invention. He realized that the pumps which were draining the mines were crude and he wanted to improve them. Thus he created the factory system and mass production. He and his business partner, Boulton, never dreamed they were about to work a transformation in civilization, the like of which the world had never before witnessed. They could not foresee that coal and steel were to become all-important factors in the daily lives of men or that nations would go to war over these commodities. They did not live to see the social and economic evils that followed their good work and that caused historians and sociologists to cry out against the evils of the modern city.

REALITY UNLIKE THE DREAM

The steam engine was transported to every place where it could be put to work. King Coal built a great empire. He held his court in the cities, which grew larger through the influx of people from small towns who had heard of the wonders performed by this new invention. The magic trumpet of King Coal too often proved to be but the false and ominous shriek of a factory whistle. Their dreams of accumulating vast wealth by letting an engine do their work frequently turned into a horrible nightmare of stark reality. They found the great city with its attractive skyscrapers and they also found forests of chimneys, crowded tenements, and slums, as well as transportation that would better suit a herd of cattle and a thousand other ills of the metropolis. That was the era of coal.

About fifty years ago this coal-mad civilization saw the birth of another innovation in the field of power. When we gaze at the power houses of Niagara Falls today and watch ton after ton of water leap down a precipice and turn a 550-ton wheel which whirls a turbine and generates power for the surrounding country, it is difficult to imagine that electricity is still in its infancy. There was a man in Menlo Park, New Jersey, who had invented an incandescent lamp, and it was rumored that he intended to light up the whole city of New York with electric lights. The newspapers called him a "wizard" and some of the conservative citizens called him other things, less complimentary. But Edison was confident that he could generate power to light a few thousand of his lamps and thus throw off the shackles of the open gas flame. Here again was an inventor, unable to foresee the tremendous possibilities of his own work. Edison was no more aware of the social and economic consequences that were to follow in the wake of the Pearl Street power plant than was Watt when he invented his steam engine. Energy was born again. But this time it was not to be confined to a wasteful, individualistic power producer. It was free and could be shot hither and thither along wires and used, at first a mile or two distant, and then with the introduction of alternating current, hundreds of miles away. A copper girdle went round the earth.

Courtesy Thomas A. Edison, Inc.
EDISON'S LABORATORY AT WEST ORANGE, N. J.
As it appeared about 1908.

NEW DEVICES FOR NEW DISCOVERIES

New devices had to be made to transmit this new discovery; and they had to be constantly improved. Electricity began to widen its field and to take the place of coal. As an infant, it struggled for life, and won. And so our minds now turn to the social effect that may well be called the second industrial revolution. Although history repeats itself, it profits by past experience.

The second industrial revolution is the first great social movement in the history of the world that was not only foreseen, but actually planned. Like many another great movement, this one had a small beginning. The electrical engineer stepped from his experimental laboratory, surrounded by four walls, into a much greater laboratory consisting of towns, villages, and rural areas in general. For a time he gave up his work in advancing what patent lawyers called the "state of the art" and looked with a questioning eye on the conditions that existed where electric power was being supplied to rural areas. He found that the small towns had not

Homer Smith photo, Chicago

A MODERN ELECTRIC POWER HOUSE

kept pace with the engineer and that such modern advances as the interconnection of central stations and the pooling of power into a few great reservoirs were unknown in most cases. The power plants were, for the most part, using obsolescent machinery, and the service that they were supplying to their customers was usually for only twelve hours out of each twenty-four.

Having found the difficulties, the electrical engineer set to work to apply modern methods to the areas in question. The small, inefficient plants were bought and closed. Power was furnished from a centralized station, with sub-stations to complement them. The small town and farm districts were supplied with power equal in every respect to that supplied to the greatest metropolis, and this twenty-four hours a day. Power in small towns can be better utilized than in large cities. Chicago, for example, uses twenty-nine per cent of its electrical resources in its electric railways, transporting workers to and from their homes. In the small town this power can be turned into productive work.

The engineer is the doctor of civilization and he has come to regard large cities as his most difficult and stubborn patients. Complications are always arising and he has scarcely set himself to the task of curing one cosmopolitan disorder when two more arise to baffle him. In this age of machine, streetcars in some of our larger cities average four miles an hour.

But industry now finds a new tool in superpower—energy of unlimited quantity, of excellent quality, and of a type that has the added advantage of availability wherever a copper wire can be strung. Having found this new tool, industry has begun to move to localities where its efficacy can best be realized.

Invention by accident rather than design has been a common phenomenon. The most famous example, perhaps, is that of Goodyear who was searching for some way to make rubber more lasting and discovered the principle of vulcanization when he accidentally dropped some rubber on a hot stove. But there are many others. And there are also some legendary accounts which are not true. Watt did not invent the separate condenser because he watched the tea kettle boiling on his mother's stove. Artists have painted this theme, but the fact is that Watt did not become interested in the steam engine until he began, as an instrument maker at the University of Glasgow, to repair a model of a steam engine. He was a trained engineer and he immediately saw the wastefulness of the Newcomen engine.

It is quite probable that Gutenberg designed his printing press after watching the wine press operate. The ubiquitous saxophone was invented as the result of an accident. Adolphe Sax placed a clarinet mouthpiece (vibrating reed) in the aperture of an ophecleide (vibrating lips) and thus was born the instrument which bears his name. Edison was playing with a telegraph repeater and, hearing the musical note when the stylus struck an indentation in the paper, he conceived the idea of a phonograph. It was a queer series of happenings which led Almon B. Strowger to invent a dial operating telephone. He was a Kansas City undertaker, totally unfamiliar with engineering, who had his suspicions that a telephone operator was conniving with one of his competitors by continually reporting Strowger's line "busy."

Strowger spent his idle moments devising a "girl-less" switch-board. His raw materials were a collar box, some pins, and a lead pencil. The automatic switching which came from this attempt developed into a system that is today such a staggering revelation of human ingenuity that even an engineer who is unfamiliar with its workings must spend days studying its intricate relays before he comprehends it.

INVENTIONS BORN OF SYNTHESIS

Inventions are usually the results of synthesis. The elements that composed the electric light were in existence long before Edison was born, but it remained for him to put them together in just the right way to invent an electric light. The handing down of these components is what historians of invention have come to recognize as the technical heritage of the inventor. Social tension, or pressure, also plays an important part. The inventor has been compared to a fuse that blows when the social tension becomes too great. Inventors, in their social and economic aspects, are much like the great poets and musicians.

Had Beethoven been a cave-man in southern France thousands of years ago, the world would never have known his great symphonies. Shakespeare wrote the way he did largely because of the age in which he lived. The Wright brothers arrived on the cosmic stage at just the moment when the fundamentals of flying were being better understood. Through the gliding experiments of Chanute and Lilienthal it had been clearly demonstrated that man could not hope to imitate the bird and fly with flapping artificial wings. Chanute had adopted the Pratt truss of the bridge builders to glider construction, and the use of the wings for support rather than locomotion was well known. On the other hand, the internal combustion engine had been developed to the point where it was light enough to be used for flying, and the principle of the propeller to screw its way through the air by alternate bites was ready for exploitation. The Wright brothers had the ingenuity to synthesize all of these things—their technical heritage—into the first man-carrying flying machine.

PART OF THE RIVERA FRESCO ON NORTH WALL, DETROIT INSTITUTE
OF ARTS, TYPIFYING THE AUTOMOTIVE INDUSTRY

THE AMAZING STORY of the growth of the cotton textile industry is one which challenges the imagination even of the modern mind. From the comparatively insignificant figure of $67,000 in 1730 to over $3,500,000,000 in 1935, English cotton production alone has increased in value over five million per cent; due to improvements in textile machinery.

Less than two hundred years ago, cotton and woolen goods were still spun and woven in the home, as they had been for centuries past, not only in England, but throughout the world. Strangely enough, there had been little mechanical improvement in this old and important industry. The eighteenth-century English woman used much the same type of hand spindle and hand loom that had been used by the spinners and weavers of ancient times.

All this was to change completely from 1770 to 1830, for as the Industrial Revolution got under way in England, the textile industry soon adopted mechanical devices in place of the old tedious hand labor.

The first important change in the traditional manufacture of textiles came with the so-called "putting-out" system, from which originated the function of the modern middleman. He contracted to provide raw materials for individuals and they in turn, for a few shillings, produced finished goods. From the sale of the latter the middleman usually made a handsome profit.

THE FLYING SHUTTLE AND THE SPINNING JENNY

This rising capitalist industry was given further impetus by the invention in 1738 of the flying shuttle by John Kay, a Lancashire weaver. He built a mechanical device which automatically brought the woof back and forth through the warp. It was so

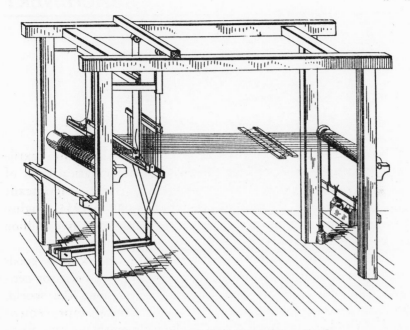

KAY'S FLYING SHUTTLE LOOM (1733)

successful that the weaver could work more rapidly than the spinner, but it did not come into popular use, due to widespread hostility to anything new. Kay's machine was destroyed by weavers who feared it would rob them of their jobs, and he was forced to flee to France where he died in poverty and obscurity.

The next improvement came logically enough in the spinning process in 1764. James Hargreaves, a weaver by trade, found himself without work, due to an insufficient supply of yarn. The story goes that one day, while waiting for his wife to spin more yarn, his daughter Jenny upset the spinning wheel. Hargreaves noticed that the wheel continued to revolve and the spindle still wound the spun thread. With this idea in mind, he began to construct a frame containing eight spindles, which allowed one person to turn a wheel and spin eight threads at a time. Hargreaves set up his "spinning jenny"—named for his daughter— in his home, but it suffered the same fate as Kay's shuttle, for his neighbors broke in and destroyed it. Undaunted, he moved to

HARGREAVE'S SPINNING JENNY

another town, rebuilt his machine, and became a wealthy manufacturer. His invention speeded up the production of cotton
thread many times. In fact, it was possible to spin 120 threads
with it as easily as one thread had been spun before.

ARKWRIGHT—THE ITINERANT BARBER-INVENTOR

To Richard Arkwright, itinerant barber, wigmaker, hair-dyer,
and horse-trader, the next important invention in cotton manufacturing is attributed. While visiting a textile factory, he
overheard a weaver complain of the unevenness of the yarn. Arkwright became interested and began to experiment with a spinning
jenny. Neither the loss of his money nor his wife's constant scold-
ings could discourage him. He enlisted the aid of a clock-maker
named Kay to make a model, and even appropriated certain principles of a machine previously invented by a mechanic named
Highs. Aware of the great hostility of the laboring classes, Arkwright and Kay worked in secret. Two old women living nearby
reported they heard terrible humming sounds as if the devil himself were tuning his bagpipes while two men were dancing a jig.

Arkwright's invention, perfected in 1769, consisted of two sets of moving rollers, one set revolving more rapidly than the other, thus drawing out and stretching the fiber before it was made into yarn. It came to be known as the water frame, for it was so heavy that only water power could turn it.

He succeeded in safeguarding his patent rights, in spite of endless legal suits of jealous inventors who claimed he had stolen their ideas. Irate mobs of unemployed burned his factories, while local police merely looked on, not daring to interfere. Arkwright persisted in his efforts, reopened his mills, bought a country estate, became a prominent local squire, and in 1786 was knighted by George III. Sir Richard, the man who nearly introduced large-scale production into the textile industry, left a fortune of £400,000. The poor itinerant barber had come a long way from his wigmaking, hair-dyeing and horse-trading days.

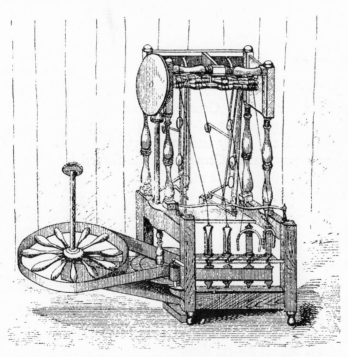

ARKWRIGHT'S WATER SPINNING FRAME CONSTRUCTED
IN 1769

SAMUEL
CROMPTON
Inventor of the
spinning mule.

Paul's Photos, Chicago

CROMPTON'S "MULE"

Despite the great progress made thus far in the textile industry, it remained for Samuel Crompton to construct a machine that would produce smooth, well-twisted thread, and thus remedy the defects of both the jenny and water frame.

When a youngster, Crompton was forced by his mother to run a spinning wheel. She scolded him each time the yarn broke, and he in desperation determined to build a machine which would spin a strong, even thread. Each evening, after playing on his home-made fiddle in the local theater for eighteen pence a performance, he came home to work secretly on his invention. The untimely light and strange sounds, which issued from his room, were grounds for the neighbors' belief that the Crompton house was haunted.

At length, in 1779, he finished what he jokingly called a "mule"—a hybrid descendant of the water frame and the spinning jenny. As its rollers drew out the yarn, the spindle moved back and stretched the thread evenly, but without breaking it.

Fearing that his machine would be destroyed by prying neighbors, he moved to another town. Unfortunately, he was not successful in safeguarding his patent, and wealthy factory owners appropriated it. He died a disappointed and poor man, but his valuable contribution to the weaving industry has never been challenged.

EDMUND CARTWRIGHT, CLERGYMAN-INVENTOR

Spinning mechanisms up to this time had developed faster than the weaving machines. This fact struck the inventive mind of the Reverend Doctor Cartwright as he visited one of Arkwright's mills in 1784. While he experimented, he told his doubting friends that the textile industry would soon see "weaving johnnies as well as spinning jennies." With the aid of a carpenter and a smith he produced in 1785 a clumsy loom, which even he admitted was inadequate, for it had to be stopped when sizing the warp. The needed remedy for this—a starch paste—was introduced by William Radcliffe in 1802.

Cartwright suffered the usual fate of the pioneer textile inventor. His factories were burned, his workmen mutinied, and his patents were stolen. Parliament, however, recognized his contribution and granted him £10,000, with which he bought a farm, and contented himself with scientific agricultural experiments until his death.

By 1820, hand weaving had been definitely supplanted by machines. Other improvements, such as the Bell cylinder for printing calicoes, used as early as 1785, and the Jacquard loom for weaving intricate brocaded patterns in silk and cotton, did much to popularize the industry.

EARLY COTTON INDUSTRY IN AMERICA

Samuel Slater, an Englishman, hoping to profit by the bounties offered new industries by the United States government, came to Providence, Rhode Island, in 1789. After many discouragements, he succeeded in building the first water-power spinning mill in

Courtesy Mei Ya Silk Mill, Shanghai

A MODERN SPINNING MILL IN CHINA

Today the latest textile-making machinery of the West is spreading rapidly
through the Far East

America at Pawtucket, Rhode Island. It stands today—a monument to the father of the American factory system.

The first cotton factory in the world which handled the whole process of textile production was established in 1813 at Waltham, Massachusetts, by Francis Cabot Lowell.

New mechanical improvements were rapidly adopted in both the spinning and weaving processes. William Crompton in 1837 perfected a loom to weave figured designs; his son, George Crompton, constructed a broad loom, which doubled the width of the cloth, while Lucius Knowles perfected both the inventions of the Cromptons in 1856.

THE MODERN LOOMS

The problem of threading the shuttle while the machine was in motion remained unsolved as late as the end of the nineteenth century. James Northrup, an English mechanic, while working in a New England textile mill, experimented successfully with devices which overcame this defect. His invention, called the Northrup loom, was a mechanism which automatically fed the yarn evenly on the shuttles and ejected the empty ones. This clever machine speeded up the weaving process, making textile production possible on a larger scale than ever.

Other devices have been constantly added which make the modern textile machinery appear almost human as it spins and weaves beautifully colored and intricately designed patterns in to silk, wool, linen or cotton fabrics. The large textile factory of today is a far cry from the primitive manufacturing plant of an Arkwright or a Slater! Yet this industry throughout its phenomenal development has pioneered the way for the modern factory system and fathered large-scale production.

Homer Smith photo, Chicago

SPINNING COTTON WITH MODERN MACHINERY

IT IS IMPOSSIBLE to estimate the countless millions whose lives have been affected by the invention of the cotton gin.

As is often the case in modern industry, continued mechanical improvement in the eighteenth-century textile machinery brought about such efficiency that the demand for raw material exceeded the supply.

The pressing problem of feeding the voracious new English spinning and weaving machines had to be met. Although much raw cotton came from India, the West Indies, and the United States, the supply was not sufficient. The planters of the southern states up to this time had specialized in raising tobacco, indigo, and rice, but now, as English factories demanded more and more raw material, their attention and interest turned to cotton culture. Georgia and the Carolinas, with their equable climate, fertile soil, and abundant slave labor, were particularly well adapted to the raising of the valuable fiber. In spite of the endless toil of the Negro, the constant goading of the overseer, and increasing anxiety of the planter, the supply was always short. In fact, in 1792, the entire cotton crop of the United States—138,234 pounds—could have been produced in a two-hundred-acre field! It was possible to increase actual production, but the tedious and costly process of separating the fiber from the seed and boll kept the marketable surplus down, and made it unlikely that cotton would ever be grown to any great extent. The laborious task of preparing the fiber for commercial use was largely performed by slaves, who at best could clean only a pound a day.

Obviously the time was ripe for a mechanical device to solve this problem. The man who was to give the solution to the eager world was a New England farmer's son, by the name of Eli Whitney.

WHITNEY— INGENIOUS INVENTOR

Courtesy Chicago Historical Society

While a young boy at his farm home in Westboro, Massachusetts, Whitney preferred tinkering in his father's well-equipped workshop to either farm tasks or school. By the time he was twelve, he had made a violin and earned local popularity by playing at country dances. Perhaps his most ambitious and ingenious achievement as a lad, however, was taking his father's watch apart. Fearing a caning if discovered, he hurriedly put it together and to his delight it ran as well as ever. This accomplishment gave him added courage to attempt other things. Before long the neighbors kept him busy repairing anything from an old violin to a broken chair.

This enterprising youth, too young to join the army when the Revolution broke out, anticipated the great wartime need for nails, by making the first successful nail machine. At the end of the war, he turned his device to making ladies' hairpins, thus continuing his profitable venture.

By this time, Whitney regretted his lack of formal schooling, and determined to attend Yale. Entering in 1789 when he was twenty-three years of age, he was able to earn a considerable portion of his expenses by repairing articles about the college. Once he mended an astronomical device, which otherwise could have been repaired only in Europe.

Upon his graduation, he decided to read law. In order to secure funds and leisure he accepted a position as tutor with a Georgia family, and presently sailed for Savannah. On the boat, the young New Englander became acquainted with Mrs. Nathanael Greene, widow of the Revolutionary officer, and her plantation overseer, Phineas Miller.

Arriving in Savannah, he was disheartened to find that his prospective employer had engaged another tutor. Mrs. Greene at once offered him the hospitality of her lovely Mulberry Grove estate, on the Savannah River. Whitney gratefully accepted, and although he intended to read law he found his time occupied with odd repair jobs on the plantation. His hostess got him to rebuild and improve her embroidery frame.

One summer evening in 1792 a group of prominent southerners were entertained at the Greene plantation. During the course of the conversation, the distressing condition of the southern cotton industry was discussed. If only some inexpensive method to clean the fiber for market could be devised! Mrs. Greene, aware of her young guest's inventive ability, remarked confidently, "Surely, Mr. Whitney can supply your needs."

Whitney took this casual suggestion seriously and the next day visited the nearby plantations, collecting samples of cotton and observing the Negroes pull the seeds off the fiber with their fingernails. He then began experimenting with a revolving cylinder equipped with two-inch teeth. These passed through narrow slits and caught the fiber, expelling the boll and seed, which were too large to pass through. Within ten days he completed his model, and Mrs. Greene proudly invited her friends to watch its operation. Filled with hopeful anticipation, they gathered around the strange machine. For the first few minutes it worked perfectly—then, to Whitney's utter chagrin, it stopped abruptly, clogged with the fibers. This difficulty he quickly solved by installing a second roller covered with stiff brushes, which revolved in the opposite direction, cleaning the cotton from the first cylinder.

Courtesy Museum of Science and Industry, Chicago

MODEL OF WHITNEY'S COTTON GIN

GREAT SCHEMES AND HARD LUCK

News of this marvelous machine, which could clean fifty pounds of cotton a day, spread swiftly. No wonder southerners came from far and near to catch a glimpse of this new mechanism that was to revolutionize the cotton industry. Most of them returned home filled with hopeful visions of great fortunes. Many planted additional acres of cotton, trusting that the inventor could get the gin on the market before harvest.

Whitney and Phineas Miller, Mrs. Greene's overseer, formed a partnership, expecting to monopolize the southern cotton industry by purchasing, cleaning, and selling the entire output, but this scheme proved impractical. Before they could perfect the model, their workroom was broken into and the machine stolen. Whitney set about building another one, but, before he received his patent in 1794, models of the stolen gin were in use throughout the South.

Hoping to have better luck in the North, Whitney and his partner went to New Haven, Connecticut, and opened a factory. Here they planned to build gins and lease them to the planters on a thirty-three and one-third per cent royalty basis. These plans met with failure, for their buildings and models burned in 1795. More discouragement was yet in store for Whitney. In 1801-1802, both South Carolina and Georgia annulled his patent rights, and, in 1812, Congress refused to renew his federal patent. Lawsuit after lawsuit, frequent tiring carriage trips to the South, and the efforts of influential friends, availed him nothing.

Refusing to bewail his misfortune, with his customary ingenuity he turned to the manufacture of firearms. Designing his own factory and machines, Whitney was the first inventor to introduce successfully the principle of interchangeable parts into industry. Before he died in 1817, a wealthy and respected citizen, he lived to see his cotton gin revolutionize the whole cotton industry. In fact, his invention was so efficient that even modern gins have made no change in the basic principle of operation.

THE COTTON GIN MAKES COTTON KING

To the inventive genius of Eli Whitney the world owes a great debt. Unquestionably there have been few inventions which have had effects as far-reaching and as significant. Literally from "India's coral strands to Greenland's icy mountains," it has influenced the political and economic life of millions. The New Englander's invention placed Great Britain definitely in the lead as the first cotton-manufacturing nation. At the present time, this supremacy is seriously threatened by Japan and the United States, yet it is possible that the tremendous output of English cotton factories may keep England ahead of her competitors for some time to come.

Perhaps the gin had its most significant reaction in the United States. One wonders if the Civil War would have occurred, if Whitney had not happened to go South and build his famous machine! His invention turned unprofitable slave labor into a priceless asset. Southerners had previously even considered freeing their slaves, but now with visions of dazzling fortunes before them they bid unheard-of prices for healthy, strong Negroes at the local auctions. This brought about an increase in the southern slave population of from 700,000 in 1790, to 4,000,000 in 1860. Since cotton culture exhausts the soil, the more ambitious planters moved westward into the fertile acres of Alabama, Mississippi, Tennessee, and Texas.

Before long, "cotton diplomacy" permeated every act and thought of southern life, and eventually plunged that section into a futile civil conflict. Thus the course of history was shaped and even determined by Whitney's epoch-making invention. It also made possible the emergence of the United States as the greatest cotton exporter, and today over half of the yearly crop of from twelve to fifteen million bales is exported to England, Japan, Germany, and France. One can readily appreciate the fact, that raw cotton is the most valuable single export of the United States, as one sees thousands of American cotton bales on London wharves, in Japanese factories, or in European munition plants.

"KING COTTON"

ONE HUNDRED YEARS AGO the arrival of a new suit or a new dress was a rare treat, and the dressmaker and the tailor were popular citizens of our towns and villages. These artisans were considered as members of a professional class, like the doctor and lawyer, and each contributed his extraordinary skill, the one adding ruffles, plaits, and flounces to the dresses of fashionable women, the other making fancy shirts, coats, and trousers for the men. Each tailor operated his own small shop where he and his assistants measured, cut, and assembled the suit that made its owner more nattily attired than the man next door who had purchased a suit two years before. The dressmaker, often a spinster or a widow, was a regular visitor to the homes of prominent citizens early in the nineteenth century. Her deft fingers designed and made the new spring dresses of the débutante and society matron. Both the tailor and the dressmaker sewed painstakingly by hand every stitch in the garment.

Even though there were specialists, whose services could be purchased by those with the means, most of the sewing and mending of clothing was done by the mother and other women in the household. Little girls learned to use the needle before they learned to read. Grandmothers frequently lived with their married children, and a familiar figure was the gray-haired old lady rocking slowly in her comfortable chair, sewing endlessly on the trousers and shirts of the men and boys. Mothers, aunts, and daughters made dresses and petticoats for themselves and for other women members of the family. More than ninety per cent of the tailoring done anywhere in the world was carried on at home by the women; ninety-nine and ninety-nine one-hundredths per cent of all sewing was hand work!

About a century ago, when Elias Howe began considering the problem of mechanical sewing, there was already a machine on the market to perform the operation. It was more like a knitting

A CHAIN STITCHING MACHINE OF 1790
The work of this machine, similar to knitting, could be unraveled by pulling
a single thread.

machine, for its stitching could easily be unraveled by pulling on a single thread—a potentially annoying and embarrassing method so far as the wearer was concerned. But inventive minds were to develop a finer, more permanent way of stitching.

Walter Hunt of New York, a visionary inventor, had already built and sold a few models of his own machine before Howe started work, but he neglected to apply for patents. Later Hunt tried to claim his share of the profits that manufacturers were earning, but he did not succeed—this despite the fact that he had contributed the basis of many machines: the lock-stitch device and the eye-pointed needle.

HOWE'S STRUGGLES

Elias Howe was a farm boy, born in Spencer, Massachusetts, on July 9, 1819. Certain members of Howe's family had already shown inventive ability: an uncle, William Howe, had invented a method of trussing roofs and bridges, and another uncle, Tyler Howe, had invented a spring bed and other devices for comfort.

Because of lameness, young Elias moved from the farm in 1835 to the cotton mills at Lowell, Massachusetts. There he found work in a machine shop where mill machinery was constructed. When the financial panic two years later stopped the mills, he went to Boston and entered the shop of Ari Davis.

Ari Davis was an eccentric inventor, of the type sometimes portrayed in the movies: he affected loud clothing and all sorts of unconventional behavior, but he was a man of ability, and numerous people asked him for aid in developing inventions. One day a client came to engage Davis as a consultant. He wanted a knitting machine. The bombastic Davis made the remark that he could invent a machine even for sewing! He failed to carry out the boast, but Howe overheard him and an idea was born.

While Howe worked over this problem, he was trying to support a wife and three children on a salary of nine dollars a week, a task in which his wife aided by taking in sewing. Howe finally thought of making a needle with an eye in the point. Although Hunt had already made such a needle, he did not patent the invention, and there is no way of showing that Howe knew of his predecessor's accomplishment.

HOWE'S SEWING MACHINE, PERFECTED IN 1846

Under the stimulation of the improvement of the eye-pointed needle, work on the sewing machine progressed much more rapidly than before. Elias gave up his job, and spent all of his time in his improvised shop. Finally a friend advanced five hundred dollars and took Howe's family into his home. In May, 1845, a model of the sewing machine was ready. Howe had a working machine that held the cloth in a vertical position; a hand wheel raised and lowered the needle, and it was quite possible to do straight-line sewing on the new machine. It was finished!

TAILORS TERRIFIED

Tailors instantly showed animosity toward the new sewing machine. They were terror-stricken at the thought of a machine that could do the work of seven tailors. They feared that only one of every seven tailors would find work to do. Capitalists, too, would have nothing to do with the new machine. No one would consider financing the young inventor. Although a patent was secured, prospects in America seemed very discouraging; so Elias Howe sent his brother Amasa to England, where he found a manufacturer who would make and sell the machines. This turned out to be an unfortunate connection, however, after Elias and his whole family went to London. The British rights were sold for about a thousand dollars, a sum which soon dwindled away. Howe and his family were soon back in America, penniless. One misfortune followed another, and Mrs. Howe died. It was even necessary for the inventor to borrow fare money to be with his wife during her last days.

Suddenly fortune smiled. The friend to whom Howe had once sold a half-interest in the invention had in turn sold it to George W. Bliss, a wealthy man, and money was forthcoming to fight the lengthy legal battles that were pending. By this time numerous companies were selling sewing machines, and it was necessary to prove patent infringement in the courts. One decision was handed down, in which the court declared that Isaac Merrit Singer should pay the inventor fifteen thousand dollars in royalties. By 1860, Howe had received more than a million dollars from his invention.

THE FIRST
SINGER SEWING
MACHINE, MAN-
UFACTURED
IN 1851
The packing case
served as a stand for
the machine.

SINGER TO THE RESCUE

Singer was the greatest promoter and merchandiser of sewing machines. A mechanic by trade, he had been a theatrical manager, and at all times he was a great showman. Previously, he had gone to Boston to work on a woodworking machine, and became interested in the sewing machine. It cost him only forty dollars to build his first model, and soon he was in the manufacturing business. Singer's showmanship came to the fore, and he had such success in marketing the machines that Howe made a great deal of money from royalties alone. Singer adopted many advertising practices that are in use today, and he was responsible for making women of America "sewing machine-conscious."

As America forged ahead, the sewing machine developed, and rough wooden frames gave way to metal and finely finished cabinets. Improvement was constant as more and more inventors took up the work. Allen Benjamin Wilson created a double-pointed shuttle and later a rotating hook that made an unusually strong lock stitch. Still later he invented a special method of feeding thread, which was later adopted in practically all machines.

James E. Gibbs, a Virginia planter, saw a magazine illustration of a sewing machine. Because most of the mechanism was hidden in the illustration, he was prompted by curiosity to build a machine himself, just to see how it worked. Unwittingly, Gibbs invented a revolving hook device. In his machine, it was necessary to employ the eye-pointed needle first invented by Hunt, and royalties were due to Howe and Wilson for the device. The Gibbs machine turned out to be one of the finest on the market for certain types of work, such as that required in the manufacture of fine lingerie.

THE SEWING MACHINE
OF TODAY

Courtesy Singer
Manufacturing Co.

Gibbs was only one of many talented people developing the sewing machine, and soon all clothing manufacturers were using sewing machines and other labor-saving devices. The end of the Civil War caused a stimulus to large-scale manufacturing of clothes, as the former soldiers clamored for new civilian clothes. Soon came the development of the West and the influx of immigration. More and more people wanted factory-made clothes, and they wanted them in a hurry.

Howe's sewing machine was operated by turning a hand wheel, and Singer's machine operated from a foot treadle. Today, most sewing machines sold for factory and home use are driven by electric motors. In factories, the machines make from three to four thousand stitches per minute, or a seam nearly fifty feet long. The simple sewing machine got its first foothold in industry in 1850. Now there are powerful new machines for stitching, button-holing, seaming, seam-closing, fronting, pressing, and labeling. Clothes-making has been removed from the chimney-corner to the specialized factory. A suit of clothes cost between one hundred fifty and two hundred dollars in 1846, but these days one may buy a ready-made suit for fifteen dollars or less.

Courtesy The Smyth Manufacturing Co.

THE SEWING MACHINE TODAY FINDS
WIDE INDUSTRIAL APPLICATIONS
This machine, used in bookbinding, stitches the
sections of a book together.

THE IMPLEMENT was little more than a crooked stick, sharpened at one end. Slaves or oxen dragged it across the field, making a shallow, crooked scratch on the soil. In another field, thousands of miles away and centuries later, a machine of iron and steel pulled by a tractor left even furrows of freshly turned loam. Each of these implements was a plow—the one in ancient Egypt, the other in modern America. Between these two devices stretched long centuries during which improvements appeared slowly.

Ancient plows usually were made of wood, although iron shares may have been used seven centuries before Christ. The Romans added a primitive moldboard to turn over the furrow and a coulter to cut the sod before the share. This type of plow had the main principles upon which modern plows are constructed. Oxen or slaves were hitched to a beam varying in length. The coulter and share cut the soil, while the moldboard turned it over. Handles were added to allow the plowman to guide the implement. A landside, added later, held the plow on a steady course. This type of device was a great advance over the crooked tree limb used in primitive agriculture, but improvements were needed.

When the Pilgrims sought refuge in Holland, they became acquainted with Dutch plows, which were the first improvements over the old Roman implement. But when they landed in Massachusetts it was necessary to imitate the Indians, or to use the cumbersome tree limb to stir the soil. Not until 1632 were real plows used in Massachusetts, and five years later there were only thirty-seven in the whole colony! They were clumsy affairs, twelve feet long, with a ten-foot beam and a four-foot landside. Eight or more oxen were required to pull this wooden contraption which did such poor work.

The Rotherham plow, which appeared in Holland about 1700, turned a more satisfactory furrow than had been obtained before;

CRUDE WOODEN PLOW
USED IN ANCIENT
EGYPT

and a Scotchman named Small added iron parts in 1730. Robert Ransome of Ipswich patented a cast-iron share in 1785, but the plow was still crude. The shares dulled quickly and broke when they hit rocks. Moldboards were unsatisfactory, and the entire machine was clumsy.

Charles Newbold of Burlington, New Jersey, at the end of the eighteenth century, turned his attention to the problem. His experiments resulted in an improvement over the Rotherham plow, and featured a cast-iron moldboard. Two oxen and one man could pull this new machine. Newbold's neighbors refused to believe even when they saw. The iron, they said knowingly, would poison their land! After spending about $30,000 on the invention, Newbold gave up in despair.

CONQUEST OF THE PRAIRIES

At about the time that Newbold was experiencing such disappointments, Thomas Jefferson and James Small studied the problem of building scientific moldboards. But their discoveries

CAST IRON PLOW
DEVELOPED IN THE UNITED
STATES, 1797

AN AMERICAN WHEEL PLOW IN USE AT THE END OF THE
NINETEENTH CENTURY

were not used until Jethro Wood, at Scipio, New York, took out
a patent in 1819 for a cast-iron plow which used wood for the
beam and handles only. When the success of Wood's invention
was assured, he became involved in costly suits to prevent patent
infringements. When he died in 1834, the prairies of the Middle
West were being broken by his cast-iron plows, which were also
being broken by the prairies!

To the person born and bred in the city it may seem peculiar
that there should be any great problem in the building of a plow
apart from the fact that it must be made of wear-resisting
materials. But a plow is something more than an instrument for
scratching the surface off the soil. It must dig deeply, cut square-
ly, lift the soil on the bottom which is rich and fertile and lay it
carefully aside as a new surface in which to plant a new crop.
More than this, it must constantly shed the soil it raises or, as the
farmer puts it, it must scour. The plow, therefore, was not only
an agricultural problem but a problem in mathematics, physics,
chemistry, metallurgy, and engineering.

A Chicago blacksmith, John Lane, tried to satisfy the need for
unbreakable shares by fixing strips of steel saw-blades to a wooden
frame. In the next year, 1834, John Deere at Grand Detour,
Illinois, became interested in the plows he was being asked to repair. Although John Deere had probably never heard of Lane,

he developed Lane's idea. Deere imported saw-steel from Germany to use for moldboards and shares. He moved to Moline in 1847, and, with a better grade of steel from the Jones and Quigg mills at Quincy, he made plows that could conquer the loam and loess of the Middle West.

The next improvements made were in the materials used to build the moldboard and the share. William Morrison, in 1868, placed a soft center of iron between two sheets of steel, making excellent moldboards. This principle was used in compound armor-plate a few years later. James Oliver, a Scotch immigrant living at Mishawaka, Indiana, bought an interest in a foundry at South Bend for less than a hundred dollars. Here he carried on experiments after 1855 in making a chilled-iron moldboard which would take a high polish and be durable. Oliver lived until 1908, and was known as one of Indiana's richest men.

Courtesy Hercules Motors Corp.

A DIESEL TRACTOR DRAWING A TEN-BOTTOM DISC PLOW

Courtesy International Harvester Co.

A MODERN HORSE-DRAWN, TWO-BOTTOM GANG PLOW

Few farmers who now ride on their tractors across the fields, turning many furrows, think of these inventors who did so much to take the drudgery out of plowing. The thousands of modern farm implements are monuments to their work, which contributed so much to the development of an efficient system of agriculture.

STRIDING across dusty fields hacked and scratched by primitive hoes and plows, the sower cast seed by hand before the era of modern drills. Brushwood was dragged over the land, covering the seed poorly. Birds used the fields as feeding grounds, and the plants that did come up were so unevenly placed that cultivation was impossible. If a bushel of seed produced as many as five bushels of grain, the farmer felt well repaid for his labor!

This wasteful broadcast method of sowing was used when "Ruth . . . sick for home . . . stood in tears amid the alien corn." Records show that the Babylonians and other early civilizations used primitive seeding devices but their use was very restricted. Throughout the Middle Ages and into modern times, hand-sowing continued.

A "CRAZY" ENGLISH FARMER

About two hundred years ago an Englishman, Jethro Tull, tried to convince farmers that there was a better way to plant cereals. He could see that rows, or "drills," were necessary to permit cultivation. Why couldn't horses be used to pull machines that would drop the seed? Tull answered the question by building a "horse-hoe." A box was mounted above a series of hoes, and the seed fell in little streams behind them. The field was then dragged to cover the grain, and Tull later added a harrow attachment to his drill. But this man, like many another great inventor, was accused of being crazy! Now, any farmer who tries to sow wheat or rye broadcast is considered even more foolish than Jethro Tull.

Americans soon tried to improve Tull's drill. Eliakim Spooner made some progress at the end of the eighteenth century, but grain dropped too fast from the seed box. A Michigan inventor, Gibbons, fed the seed into "shoes," and in 1842 the Pennocks in Pennsylvania patented a device to control the method of feeding. This drill was produced in quantities after the Civil War. Now there

Courtesy International Harvester Co.

A GRAIN DRILL WHICH PLANTS TWENTY-TWO ROWS IN
ONE TRIP ACROSS THE FIELD
Note the chains which cover the seeds with earth.

are two boxes on many drills: one for commercial fertilizer and
the other for seed. Discs make little ditches into which the grain
is dropped, and chains or other devices drag on the ground to cover
both fertilizer and seed.

On the huge wheat-growing ranches in different parts of the
world, tractors pull discs, harrows, and drills which prepare the
soil and plant the crop in one operation. Huge elevators, grain
ships, freight cars, and gigantic flour mills testify to the vision of
Jethro Tull, the "crazy" English farmer.

When the first English settlers came to America they found a
number of valuable crops. Pumpkins, squashes, and corn were
cultivated by the red men, who taught the whites their rude skills.
Indian corn was planted by hand in soil laboriously scraped into
hills by the squaws. A fish was added for fertilizer, and a watcher
tried to keep away the avaricious crows. Since that time corn has
become one of the world's greatest crops. Corn is put to so many
different uses, is grown so widely, and is such a valuable crop that
agriculture, industry, and business would be disrupted without it.

Thousands of corn planters are busy in the spring of the year, making rhythmical "clicks" as they go across the fields. There is a story behind those "clicks," a story of struggle and disappointment, failure and success.

The grain drill was not satisfactory for planting corn, which should be placed in evenly-spaced "hills" to allow thorough cultivation. Hand planters were an improvement over the Indian practice, but they were too slow. D. S. Rockwell solved the problem with a two-row, horse-drawn planter in 1839. But something more was needed—an invention that would drop the corn so that there would be rows across the field at right angles. This kind of planting would permit the farmer to cultivate on four sides of the hills and eliminate the weeds within the rows. Just before the Civil War, in 1857, Robins' check-wire planter solved the problem, but the inventor did not live to perfect it. John Thompson and John Ramsay, two Illinois inventors, took out patents in 1864 on an improved check-wire planter, and the Haworth brothers made it a commercial success. The modern corn planter unreels a long, knotted wire and as it moves across the field the knots in the wire trip the mechanism to do the planting at regular intervals.

Hundreds of thousands of acres, with millions and millions of corn stalks make beautiful green patches on the landscape throughout the United States. Countless hogs and cattle crowd greedily around the feeding troughs. Experiment stations with busy scientists are maintained in the corn belts. Factories make starch, mucilage, sugar, syrup, oil, and other products from the millions of bushels that are harvested in the corn fields. And behind all these activities are the corn planter and the check-wire, humble reminders of what forgotten men have done.

THE CORN
PLANTER
AT WORK
Showing the all-important checkwire which spaces the distance between seeds.

Courtesy International
Harvester Co.

SICKLES, SCYTHES, AND EARLY REAPERS

TILLING THE SOIL is one of the oldest of the arts, and the growing of grains has a story almost as old as man. Archaeologists digging in the ruins of forgotten civilizations uncover grains of wheat and sickles used to cut the plants. These early cutting devices were made of stone and later of bronze.

Both the scythe, part of the equipment on nearly every modern farm, and the mighty, intricate combine, had ancestors existing at the time of Christ. Half-savage Gauls are supposed to have used a crude reaper which embodied two of the main principles of the modern reaper. They hitched an ox behind a cart with a long, knife-like blade mounted on its front edge. A worker walked beside the machine and knocked the grain against the cutter. The Romans, conquerors of the Gauls, developed the scythe by putting a long handle on a wide, straight blade.

For hundreds of years those who toiled in the fields used the back-breaking sickle and the clumsy scythe. Jules Breton in "The Song of the Lark" painted an enraptured peasant girl with a sickle in her hand. A Scotchman about 1794 thought he had solved the problem of reaping when he added a wooden rack to the scythe. This "cradle," as it was called, would catch the stalks of grain and leave it in piles, later to be picked up, bound by hand, and carried to the threshing floor. Two acres a day might be cut with the cradle. The cradle and the plain scythe were used widely in America and elsewhere even after 1850. They were cheap, not too difficult to operate, and cut the straw clean. But they were slow. Improved plows and drills could prepare many more acres of small-grain fields than the farmer could harvest with his old scythe, dating back to the days of Roman slaves.

Who would invent a practical reaper which would speed up harvesting? A minister, a teacher, a sailor, a farmer, and mechan-

Courtesy International Harvester Co.
REAPING WITH A SICKLE, THE FIRST HARVESTING TOOL

Courtesy International Harvester Co.

THE CRADLE
Developed at the end of the eighteenth century; the bars caught the grain cut
by the scythe and left it in piles.

CYRUS HALL McCORMICK
Builder of the first practical reaper.

ics, all contributed ideas. An Englishman, Salmon of Woburn,
took out a patent in 1807 for a machine with a moving knife and
a self-raker. Another Englishman, Henry Ogle, built a reaper
thirteen years later. He also used a sliding knife, and added a reel
to force the stalks against the knife and dividers to separate them
into small bunches. Patrick Bell, a Scotch minister, decided that a
series of scissors would cut cleaner than the sliding knife. Bell's
reaper carried the cut grain to one side on a canvas belt moving on
wooden rollers. The belt and the rollers are still indispensable parts
of the modern machine. Farm hands feared that Bell's invention
would take away their harvest jobs, so they demolished their
mechanical competitor.

McCORMICK'S IDEA

In the hilly farm lands of Virginia, far from centers of population, Robert McCormick turned his inventive genius to building
a machine that would lighten the labor of harvesting. His son
Cyrus was to succeed where he himself failed. After struggling
with the clumsy contrivance for some time, the young McCormick gave it a trial in 1831, but did not take out a patent until

Courtesy International Harvester Co.

McCORMICK'S ORIGINAL REAPER

three years later. This early reaper had the seven essential principles used by modern machines: a straight knife with serrated edge to cut the grain; fingers to hold the stalks from slipping sideways; a revolving reel; a platform to carry the cut grain; a master wheel which carried the machine and furnished power for all the movement; forward draft from the right side; and a divider "to separate the grain to be cut from that to be left standing."

In Cincinnati, Ohio, far from McCormick's workshop at Walnut Grove Farm, a mechanically minded sailor and candle-maker also built a reaper. This interesting seaman was Obed Hussey, who took out a patent in 1833. A description of this reaper was published in the *Mechanics Magazine* in 1834, and revealed some of the principles developed by McCormick in 1831. Cyrus wrote to the editor and claimed "priority to these principles." Hussey later acknowledged that McCormick's rights antedated his own. Although he built his machines for a few years, Hussey could not stand the competition, and in 1858 he sold out to some of McCormick's other rivals for $200,000.

Meanwhile, the McCormicks encountered difficulty in making and selling their machines. They mined iron ore in the Alleghanies and built a blast furnace for their own use. The panic of 1837 almost ruined the enterprise. A buyer was found in 1840 who was willing to risk thirty dollars to buy a reaper. Not a machine was sold in 1841, but seven found buyers in the next year, when the price was raised to one hundred dollars. Sales mounted slowly, and Cyrus McCormick took a trip through the Middle West to spread the gospel of the reaper. There he saw wonderful farm lands and dreamed of wide fields of grain harvested by his machines.

In order to be nearer the market and also a supply of materials, the factory was moved to Cincinnati in 1845, and then to Chicago in the next year. There William Ogden bought a half-interest for $25,000. With this new capital, a thousand machines were built in 1849. Ogden's share was bought out, and the world's greatest factory for agricultural implements was well under way.

Courtesy International Harvester Co.

THE RUDE WORKSHOP IN WHICH McCORMICK BUILT THE MACHINE
WHICH REVOLUTIONIZED AGRICULTURE

Courtesy International Harvester Co.

A TRACTOR PULLING TWO AUTOMATIC BINDERS

THE BINDER

Bell, Hussey, and McCormick had found out how to cut wheat, oats, and rye quickly and well. But there was a serious defect. Men had to follow the machine and bind the grain into sheaves. This process was arduous, expensive, and inefficient. The Marsh brothers at De Kalb and John F. Hollister at Plano, Illinois, in 1857, devised an elevator on the reaper to carry the grain up to a bin where men could tie the sheaves. One more step was necessary: a mechanical binder. John F. Appleby of Wisconsin invented a twine knotter in 1858, and built a successful model nine years later. Others entered the field and in a few years the wire binder was being used. Although wire was a poor material, especially because it damaged stock and was scattered over the farms, it enjoyed one significant advantage over twine as a binding material: grasshoppers and crickets were not equipped with wire-snippers, much to the satisfaction of farmers. The appetizing nature of twine was later changed by a chemical treatment which made it unpalatable. William Deering was so impressed with Appleby's twine-binder that he bought its patent and combined it with the Marsh harvester which he also owned. The binding reaper was a reality. Now there are devices which not only cut and bind the grain, but set it in shocks as well.

When the fields of wheat, oats, and rye turn from green to golden yellow, the farmer no longer takes out the sickle and the scythe. Instead, he hitches a team of horses or a tractor to the binder and moves into the field. The many-bladed reel revolves on an axle, pressing the grain against a swiftly moving sickle-bar. The grain falls on a moving canvas, is carried against an elevator and down against "packers." At regular intervals a curved arm darts up bearing twine that is tied and cut with marvelous speed and accuracy. "Kickers" whirl around and throw the bundle onto a carrier which is tripped to lay the sheaves in rows. Then they are picked up and stood in groups called "shocks" to dry until a bundle wagon takes them to a threshing machine.

THE THRESHER AND THE COMBINE

Early threshing scenes, whether in ancient Egypt or early nineteenth-century America, were interesting to the onlooker but hardly entertaining to the laborers. Several devices were used to separate the kernels from the heads of small grain. One method was that of driving animals around and around over the sheaves until the heads were shattered. This practice, centuries old, was in use until comparatively recent times. A threshing-sledge, consisting of rollers mounted on a frame, was sometimes used to separate grain from straw. The most common method depended on the flail, which was made of two sticks fastened together loosely at one end. The flail was raised over the head and brought down with great force on the sheaves. This clumsy method produced only from five to ten bushels of wheat in a day, while dust and chaff rose in clouds to the discomfort of the laborer.

The first emancipator of those who "rode the flails" was Andrew Meikle, a Scotch mechanic who built a threshing machine in 1786. Meikle included in his thresher the principles which later

THE HAND FLAIL, 1879

inventors had to adopt. The sheaves were spread out in a feeder with the heads facing forward. They passed between two rollers and then over a rapidly turning cylinder upon which were attached beaters to strike the heads. The straw then passed under and over two other cylinders which were mounted above screens through which the grain dropped. Chaff and bits of straw fell into the grain hopper, making it necessary to fan the threshed grain. Meikle combined a fanning mill with the thresher in 1800, but the machine was so clumsy that it had to be kept in one place. Portable threshers were sold in some quantity, and fanning mills were built to which farmers could take their grain.

These machines were introduced into the United States about 1825, and the portable ones were especially in demand. American threshers were called "Ground Hogs," and were run by horsepower. Attempts were made to combine the harvester and the thresher, and Samuel Lane patented such an invention in 1828. Lane's machine was a failure, and he spent the last part of his life

AN 1879 STEAM HARVESTER AND THRESHER
Steam was applied before the coming of the tractor as a source of power.

Courtesy International Harvester Co.

MODERN THRESHING MACHINE
Showing how power is supplied by a tractor.

Courtesy Buffalo Museum of Science, Buffalo

COMBINE
A model of a harvester-thresher. The straw is spread over the field by dropping behind.

Courtesy International Harvester Co.

MASS-PRODUCTION FARMING

On the broad, flat plains of the West, great installations of modern machinery make farming
a mass-production industry. This is a fleet of twelve harvester-threshers on a wheat ranch
in western Kansas.

in an almshouse. However, inventors persisted in their efforts to
construct a combination harvester, thresher, and fanning-mill.

Hiram and John Pitts in Maine made some improvements on
the thresher in the eighteen-thirties, especially in the way in which
straw was shaken and thrown off. Their machine collected the
grain in a trough and then carried it to a fanning-mill attachment. Jacob Wemple contributed flat, bolted teeth to the cylinder
to take the place of the old wooden ones which were both dangerous and unsatisfactory. George Westinghouse, whose son invented
the air-brake, was Wemple's partner. Together they built machines that were far better than the old "Ground Hogs." Straw-
racks, used as shakers, were notched by John Nichols, and, shortly after the Civil War, the Nichols and Shepard threshers were in
common use. The blower, a long, telescoping metal tube with a
powerful fan at the base, was attached about 1880, and the threshing machine was essentially complete.

Modern inventive genius has succeeded in building a combined harvester and thresher, popularly called a "combine." These mechanical wonders can cut a sixteen-foot swath, thresh and deliver the grain in a bin or sacks, and spread the straw, all in one operation. In fact, they do almost everything except make flour and bake the bread. Tractors pull these machines easily, and an independent motor furnishes power for threshing.

CORN HARVESTERS

Modern farming requires the use of other complicated harvesting machines which would require many pages to describe. Recent years have seen the corn picker grow rapidly in favor. Corn husking used to be an all-winter job. Men walking beside a wagon tore the ears from the husks with skilful manipulation of a peg or hook strapped to the hand. A fast husker could "shuck" from eighty to one hundred bushels in a day, covering perhaps two acres. The modern streamlined corn picker, pulled by a tractor, harvests one or two rows at a time. A steady

Courtesy International Harvester Co.

THE LAST WORD IN MECHANIZED FARMING
A one-row corn picker which picks, husks, and loads corn.

Courtesy Museum of Science and Industry, Chicago

THE COTTON PICKER
A device destined to revolutionize the lives of millions of hand laborers.

stream of ears drops into a wagon, and in one day's work as many as eight to twenty acres may be covered, producing from three hundred to a thousand bushels. Another corn-harvesting machine is a special binder that cuts and binds the stalks into bundles and loads them on a wagon. Dairy cows consume great quantities of ensilage—finely chopped corn which is stored in silos. This feed may now be produced by a combination harvester and ensilage cutter in the field, after which it is blown into the silos by another specialized machine.

THE COTTON PICKER

The picking of cotton is an art that saw no advance from the earliest times to the twentieth century. So standard had become the familiar picture of the moving backs of the slaves and freemen who plucked the fluffy white bundles from the broken pods that in song, story, and art it has played an important role.

The basic problem which has always faced the inventor who would make a machine to pick cotton, is that a machine cannot differentiate between the cotton and the parts of the plant. But even that problem seems well on the way toward solution. Although there are no mechanical cotton pickers in commercial operation today, there are at least two basic types which will doubtless be in use in the not far distant future.

The cotton picker most familiar to the public today, because of the widespread publicity which it has received, is that of the Rust brothers. This device is pulled by a tractor over the cotton fields and its revolving spindles, moistened with water, entwine the cotton around themselves, tear it from the plant, and deposit it in a receiver. The other type, an experimental device of the International Harvester Company, catches the cotton on rotating dry spindles, fitted with tiny teeth, and passes it along to a doffing mechanism which removes it, after which it is partially cleaned and taken to the gin.

While these machines have been developed to the point where they pick most of the cotton from the plants which pass through their mechanisms, they also carry much of the plant refuse along with them. When this problem has been solved, as it undoubtedly will be, the mechanical cotton picker will move into the cotton belt and quickly do the work that is now carried on by human beings. One of the chief reasons why this device has received so much notice is the fact that it will displace a large number of laborers when it is perfected. That it will create technological unemployment for a time cannot be denied. But any student of the history of invention will admit that this has been true of every important innovation. We may, therefore, confidently expect that, as in thousands of other cases, this problem will be solved in ways of which we now know nothing.

JUST AS THE RENAISSANCE in trade and industry drove adventurous men across trackless continents and uncharted seas, it led other men in a less dramatic search for wealth to dig deep into the black regions beneath the surface of the earth, bringing to light hidden minerals more precious than the cinnamon and rubies of the Orient. By the eighteenth century the need for copper and coal had pitted England with deep open mines. But, as men burrowed deeper and deeper, an obstacle more difficult to combat than solid rock rose to block their progress; that obstacle was water. Collecting after rains and seeping through into the lower workings, it shut off access to the rich veins until a way was found to drain it out.

So great was the need for mineral products that men and horses were put to work pumping the water or carrying it out in buckets, but men and horses grow tired, and their unassisted strength avails but little against the might of nature. Water triumphed in many mines, and they were abandoned. Some machine, tireless and stronger than man, was necessary if England's mines were to go on yielding the materials with which an industrial society cannot do without.

THE FIRST PUMP WAS A BOTTLE

Steam filled the need, and the story of the steam engine is inextricably bound up with the name of James Watt. Watt's fame rests on his improvements which made the engine truly practical and efficient, rather than on the discovery of the first principle. Few of the inventions which have changed the world have been the work of a single man. What was probably the earliest design for a steam engine was nineteen hundred years old when Watt applied for his patent, for an Alexandrian Greek named Hero had

built a crude steam turbine, although he made no further experiments and the scheme was
quite impractical. But appropri-
ately enough the eighteenth century, which saw the beginnings
of modern industry, ushered in
the first practical steam engine,
patented by Captain Thomas
Savery in 1698.

The manner in which Savery,
according to legend, discovered
the power of steam is an interesting story. Sitting in an inn, he
threw a nearly empty bottle
into the fireplace. The container
filled with steam, and when he
noticed this he grasped it by the
neck and plunged it upside down
into a basin of water. The steam
condensed, leaving a partial vacuum in the bottle, and water

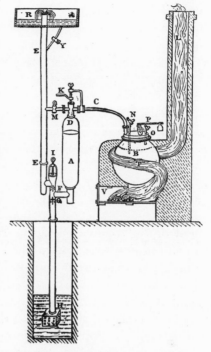

WORKING DIAGRAM OF SAVERY'S
ENGINE

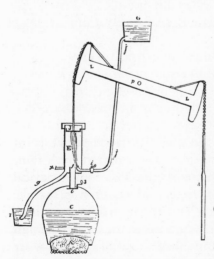

DIAGRAM OF NEWCOMEN'S ENGINE

rushed in, rising above its level
in the basin partly to fill the bottle. Thus, it is supposed, did
Savery discover the principle on
which he built his steam engine,
which was soon in use raising
water in mines and water works.

Savery's steam engine operated by allowing steam to enter an
inclosed vessel, forcing water out
and up through a one-way valve.
Cold water was then injected into
the steam-filled chamber, and,
as the steam condensed, the water
below was sucked into the vac-

uum through another valve and was again forced upward by more steam. The height to which water could be raised by this method was limited, however, and about the year 1710 a new type of engine appeared, the work of Thomas Newcomen. It was a needful refinement of Savery's engine because it introduced the action of a piston moving in the cylinder. Thus the steam was not prematurely condensed by direct contact with the surface of the water, and a great saving of fuel was effected in the elimination of steam pressure waste.

THE LID OF A TEAKETTLE

But though these men and others contributed to the development of the steam engine, the name James Watt and the phrase, "inventor of the steam engine," will always be synonymous. In Watt's practical brain and skilled hands the crude pumping engine of his predecessors evolved into an efficient machine capable of many uses—introducing thereby the Machine Age. James Watt was born in 1738, the son of a shipbuilder in Greenock, Scotland. In his father's shop young James early displayed the mechanical skill which was to influence so profoundly the life of the world. A workman in the shop was once led to remark, "Wee Jamie hae a fortune in his fingers an' anither in his head." The story of young Watt's observing the teakettle is universally familiar, even though it is probably pure fiction.

As a young man Watt by his mechanical skill secured a position as instrument maker at the University of Glasgow; while he was working there a model of the Newcomen engine was sent to him by the university for repairs. He put it into working order, but the difficulties he encountered made it clear to him that improvements were necessary and possible. After five years of patient study and experiment, he applied for a patent on his improvements in 1769. One difficulty with the Newcomen engine, Watt had reasoned, was that each time cold water was sprayed into the cylinder to condense the steam, the cylinder was cooled and the energy of the next injection of steam was partially lost because it had first to rewarm the cylinder. Accordingly he had worked out a system to keep the cylinder as hot as the steam which entered it. He attached a new chamber to the engine, a condenser, which received the steam from the cylinder, and into which the cold water was sprayed without affecting the heat of the cylinder. In addition Watt placed a metal jacket around the cylinder, leaving a space through which steam was forced; so that steam temperature was constantly maintained in the cylinder. The efficiency of the improved engine greatly reduced fuel consumption.

BACK TO THE MINES

Watt had by this time interested Matthew Boulton, the owner of a large hardware factory, in his steam engine. By 1775 Boulton secured an extension of Watt's patent for twenty-five years, and the firm of Boulton and Watt was formed.

The efficiency of Watt's condensing engine soon proved itself in actual operation. The mines adopted it and displaced the Newcomen engine, and many mines which had been at the point of

Courtesy Deutches Museum, Munich

AN EARLY ROTATING ENGINE MANUFACTURED BY BOULTON AND WATT

abandonment were enabled to resume production when the problem of water pumping was solved. Boulton and Watt made an interesting business arrangement with the mines which replaced Newcomen's engine with Watt's—one-third of the saving in fuel consumption was to be turned over to the inventing firm, and the saving often amounted to as much as seventy-five per cent.

But the engine still remained a simple pump, and Watt saw that this puffing, iron-muscled worker could be made far more useful if a way could be devised to make it turn a wheel. Although the mine-pumping problem was solved, there remained the vaster difficulty of supplying power to other new machines which were everywhere springing up, and which were limited to the use of the primitive water-wheel for energy. By 1781 Watt had worked out five different ways to convert the simple reciprocating motion of the ordinary steam engine into a rotary motion which could turn a machine drive shaft, and in that year he applied for his second patent.

Boulton and Watt prospered as their steam engine found wider and ever wider acceptance. In 1800, when his patent rights came to an end, Watt retired to a country estate and spent the rest of his life quietly working on various other mechanical problems. He died in 1819, one of the few inventors who have lived to enjoy the fruits of their efforts to contribute to the industrialization of the world.

WORKING UP MORE STEAM

Among other early workers in the field of applying steam to mechanical problems were Jonathan Hornblower, who as early as 1781 made use of the expansive qualities of steam in a beam engine with compound cylinders; Richard Trevithick, who with his "Cornish boiler" and high pressure one-cylinder engine made one of the first applications of steam to the problems of land transportation; Oliver Evans, who did much the same work in America; and Arthur Woolf, who in 1804 revived the compound engine after Hornblower had been sued out of business for patent violation by Boulton and Watt.

Courtesy Allis-Chalmers Company

A MODERN STEAM ENGINE

The development of steam power saw wide use of the beam engine, first employed by Newcomen, which is still sometimes used in ferryboats (though rarely elsewhere). The effort in this type of engine was applied at some point along one-half of the length of a rocking horizontal beam, which resembled a teeter-totter, the opposite end of which was geared or otherwise connected to turn a driving shaft. From the beginning there was a tendency to increase the pressures under which steam was used; Watt's engine employed a pressure only slightly greater than that of the atmosphere, but through the years, as metal construction improved, boiler and cylinder pressure increased tremendously in most types of engines. The double-acting cylinder was utilized to a growing extent; in this device, steam was taken in alternately by ports on either end of the cylinder to exert force on both sides of the piston. The compound engine of Hornblower, Woolf, and others was a two or more cylinder machine in which steam was first expanded in the small cylinder to produce driving force, and then it was admitted into the other, larger, chamber where the additional expansion contributed to the efficiency of steam operation. Another advantage of this type of design, which has continued increasingly in use, was that stresses resulting from wide temperature fluctuations in the boiler were reduced.

OVERCOMING THE DEAD POINT

Steadier performance was achieved by two devices which evened steam pressure from revolution to revolution and also during the revolution itself. The governor, as early as the time of Watt, when the theory of combustion and steam was primitive, was used to maintain uniform steam pressure in the engine. The flywheel is an immense, ponderous wheel which, by its great inertia in turning, levels out variations in piston action. There is a dead point in each piston stroke each time it stops and reverses direction, and the flywheel carries the drive of the engine over these dead points by sheer momentum, and, holding back somewhat in the maximum part of the stroke, it stores this energy for the next dead point. The beam engine has been replaced almost entirely by the direct-acting engine in which the piston itself acts to turn the shaft.

Further modifications have been brought about in the development of the many types of steam engine used today. Coupled, compound, and uniflow engines as well as the great steam turbines have brought stationary-engine power production to a high degree of efficiency. One of the most famous kinds is the marine engine, a powerful, widely used, direct-acting type with a surface condenser which makes use of the sea water in cooling. Another of the well-known modern stationary engines is the pumping engine; some monsters of this type can pump as much as fifty million gallons a day.

THE STEAM LOCOMOTIVE

A TRICYCLE WITH A BOILER

THE STEAM LOCOMOTIVE is a vehicle which moves along rails under its own power, that of compressed steam. With the invention of steam engines by Watt and others it was inevitable that men should try to utilize the stationary engine to provide power for a new type of mechanical transportation. Newton suggested the notion nearly a hundred years before any actual application of the principle was made. In 1769 Nicolas Cugnot, a Frenchman, made a three-wheeled tractor for the hauling of artillery. The boiler hung in front of the foremost wheel, and the engine ran on roads at a speed of two or three miles an hour. Its supply of steam lasted for only about fifteen minutes, however, at the end of which time it stopped, a fire had to be built, and more steam produced. This peculiar machine came to an ignominious end when it crashed into a stone wall. Sporadically there were similar experiments including those of Murdock,

CUGNOT'S STEAM ENGINE
First vehicle in the world to move by steam power.

Courtesy Baltimore and Ohio R.R.

MODEL OF THE "PIONEER," AMERICA'S FIRST RAILROAD CAR

one of Watt's assistants, but it remained for the next century to produce any more significant developments in steam locomotion.

Horse-drawn cars had for some time been operated on rails, and with the invention of a steam-driven road locomotive it was only a matter of time before the two devices were combined and a steam locomotive made to run on rails. In 1801 Richard Trevithick, a Cornishman, demonstrated a "tramwaggon"; two years later another of his locomotives, capable of hauling ten tons of coal, was in operation in the Welsh mines. Trevithick continued to improve his machine, and in the next year its capacity was increased to forty tons. It was powered by a single cylinder and four driving wheels, and engine efficiency was increased by running the exhaust steam through the smokestack. Early work on the steam locomotive was, almost without exception, done in connection with mining. The Trevithick rights were bought by Fenton, Murray, and Wood, of Leeds, and their improvement, the Blenkinsop colliery locomotive, was in use in 1812. Hedley's famous "Puffing Billy" appeared in the next year, and in 1814 George Stephenson brought forth his "Blucher," first of a renowned line of Stephenson engines. In 1829 his "Rocket," drawing a passenger carriage, attained a speed of twenty-four miles an hour. This "Rocket" was the first practical locomotive and is always regarded as the grandfather of the long line of "Iron Horses" that came after it.

Courtesy Baltimore and Ohio R.R.

BRUNTON'S STEAM HORSE
It was moved by the legs at the rear which pushed it forward, but the rate of speed
was too slow for practical use.

Courtesy Baltimore and Ohio R.R.

STEPHENSON'S "ROCKET"
World-famous as the first practical steam locomotive.

Courtesy Baltimore and Ohio R.R.

THE "TOM THUMB"

This engine, built by Peter Cooper, was the first successful steam locomotive in America.

"TOM THUMB" PUSHED HIS PASSENGERS

The first locomotive operated in the New World was the "Stourbridge Lion," which was imported from England in 1829; in the same year Peter Cooper began work on the first locomotive built in the United States. The famous "Tom Thumb" was only an experiment to ascertain whether Cooper could construct a working steam locomotive. It was a tiny engine, made with improvised parts such as musket barrels, used for flues; but in 1830 the little experiment pushed an open passenger car from Baltimore to Ellicott's Mills and back, a distance of thirteen miles, at an average speed of a little more than eleven miles an hour. In the next year

Courtesy Baltimore and Ohio R.R.

A FAMOUS EARLY LOCOMOTIVE, THE "ATLANTIC," WITH ITS CARS
This locomotive ran in actual service for sixty years, and is still capable of
running under its own steam.

Courtesy Baltimore and Ohio R.R.

THE SOUTH CAROLINA DOUBLE-ENDER, 1833
The first articulated locomotive, forerunner of the tremendous giants of the Mallet type.

Courtesy Baltimore and Ohio R.R.
THE "THATCHER PERKINS"
An engine of the type known as the "Iron Horse."

Phineas Davis built the "York," which had four driving wheels, an improvement of the "Tom Thumb's" two. Like those of many of its successors, the "York's" boiler was an upright cylinder. After the "York" came other famous pioneering experiments in locomotive construction, among which were the "Thomas Jefferson," the "Atlantic," and Matthew Baldwin's "Ironsides." The last, built in 1832, remained in service for twenty years. The first locomotive with a horizontal boiler, the design on which the mighty steam giants of the present are based, was the "William Galloway," built in 1837. It was also characterized by the possession of six wheels, of which two were drivers. An early type of locomotive which was an offshoot from the main line of engine-design development was the "Camel Back," made in 1848 by Ross Winans. In this variant the cab was placed atop the horizontal boiler, like the bridge of a ship; the locomotive was largely used in the hauling of freight. After a few years of experiment with this freight engine, the number of wheels was increased to ten, of which six were drivers. Various inventions increased the efficiency and speed of locomotives as their development continued. The "iron horse" style, used in Civil War days, is famous, with its bulbous stack, ungainly long-roofed cab, huge drive wheels, and tapering boiler.

MOGULS, MIKADOS, AND MALLETS

Until the general acceptance of Whyte's classification of locomotives (a simple number sequence denoting the total number of
wheels—forward truck, drivers, and trailing truck), the railroads vied with one another in the use of flamboyant names for
their engines. In the Whyte nomenclature the Mikado type, for
example, with two wheels in the pilot truck, two in the trailing
truck, and four pairs of drivers, was simply described as a 2-8-2
type locomotive. But before this system came into general use
locomotives were individually numbered and named, named according to type, and designated by the name of the line and construction date. Thus the Baltimore and Ohio's "2400," built in
1904, was called the "J. E. Muhlfeld," styled a compound articulated Mallet type, and to cap it all was nicknamed "Old Maud."
The Mogul type, now known simply as a 2-6-0, carried one pair
of wheels in the forward truck and three pairs of drivers joined

Courtesy New York Central Lines

A FAMOUS LOCOMOTIVE

No. 999, which hauled the Empire State Express forty years ago. Here it is seen taking on
water from a trough between the tracks, thus saving the time consumed in a stop.

Courtesy Northern Pacific Railway Co.
ENGINE OF THE MALLET TYPE
Its 125-foot length and weight of 1,118,000 pounds make it the largest in the world.
It is used in hauling freight over mountain grades.

by a connecting rod so that all three would move in unison, with the piston shaft from the cylinder attached to the center of the connecting rod. The force of the piston was applied to a point on the face of the wheel between the axle and rim, and a counterbalance weighted the opposite side of each wheel. In the Consolidation type the piston rod was joined to the third of four pairs of connected driving wheels. The Mallet type was really two locomotives in one, with two sets of cylinders and pistons set one behind the other, each driving three pairs of wheels.

There were many other styles: Atlantic, Mountain, Pacific, Mastodon, Santa Fe, Decapod, Prairie, and so forth. Each was

Courtesy Baltimore and Ohio R.R.
THE "GEORGE H. EMERSON"
The frame of this four-cylinder locomotive, the first of its type ever built, is a single casting sixty feet long.

designed to meet some specific problem in the fields of high- and low-speed hauling of passengers and freight over all sorts of terrain. During the nineteenth and early twentieth centuries the railroads spread a vast and comprehensive network of rails over the entire United States until the nearly a quarter-million miles of American railways included one-third of all the world's mileage. This was nearly five times as much roadbed as Russia had constructed, and Russia was the closest competitor. Endless difficulties in road construction had to be met. Railroads crossed deep gorges on spidery trestles, tunneled under mountains, bridged great arms of the sea and wide lakes, sped under mighty cities, and crossed jungles and Arctic wastes.

The locomotive attained greater speed and power by the introduction of new devices for increasing the production and pressure of steam; at the time the employment of steam multiplied into myriad uses besides the actual operation of the driving wheels. Self-produced steam power operated many innovations in the engine which added to its efficiency: generators, stokers, grate shakers, and lubricating systems; as well as such comfort and safety improvements as rail sanders, heaters, brakes, snow flanges, and air-conditioning plants. Probably best known of all the extra uses to which steam was put is the eternally familiar wail of the whistle.

NEW LABYRINTHS FOR OLD

The complexity of the locomotive's mechanism is overwhelming. From the tender car, behind the engine, flow two streams— one of coal which is fed by hand or by automatic stokers into the enormous brick-arched fire grate; the other, a stream of water, is pumped into a maze of tubing which makes the old Cretan labyrinth look like a highway. Here, and in the superheating chambers, steam is heated to temperatures as high as 750 degrees Fahrenheit. The pressure at which this steam is maintained is tremendous. When in 1831 the "York" won a competition for operating efficiency, the contest rules specified a boiler pressure not to exceed one hundred pounds to the square inch, but in modern boilers pressures greater than 250 pounds are not uncom-

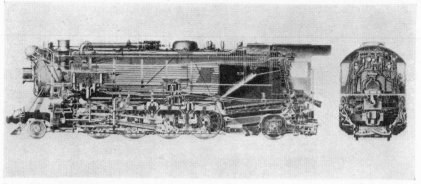

Courtesy Lima Locomotive Co.
A PHOTOGRAPHIC DIAGRAM SHOWING THE CONSTRUCTION
OF A LOCOMOTIVE

mon, and some locomotives have been built to utilize gauge pressures as high as 650 pounds. The high efficiency of this highly compressed, superheated steam was carried to almost unbelievable lengths by the German State railways, one of whose engines operated with a working steam pressure of seventeen hundred pounds.

The water is fed into the boiler by means of a steam injector, an invention first demonstrated in 1859 by Henri Giffard, in France. This device, constantly improved by later inventors, uses steam pressure to force water into the boiler against the intense internal compression. In producing the necessary force, exhaust steam, given tremendous velocity by being induced into a vacuum, is supplemented by a jet of live steam. The grate area in the firebox section has been increased to a point at which eighty and ninety square feet of combustion surface are not uncommon in the larger locomotives. In the familiar firebox arrangement the water tubes were braced between flat metal sheets arrayed in a radial system. However, the desire for greater heat absorption led to the introduction of a new style of water tube arrangement which to a considerable extent replaced the older "water-log" variety. In one of the variations of this innovation—the "Scotch tube" type—a double row of parallel vertical tubes extends to an overhead cylindrical steam drum. The steam is further heated by passing through the superheating apparatus, whose principal feature is a pipe which curves through the smokestack and in which additional heat is absorbed from the hot, smoky air.

THE CREAM THAT PUSHES THE CHURN HANDLE

Heated and superheated until it is under tremendous pressure, the steam passes through a vent in the forward end of each of the cylinder chambers, where it forces the disk of the piston backward. This action exerts a force, through the piston rod, on the driving wheels, which turns them around through half a revolution. The counterbalance weights on the wheels then drive the piston again forward, by their turning inertia, to a point at which steam, entering a vent in the other, the rear end of the cylinder, forces the disk all the way back to its original position. This takes the wheels through another half revolution. The action of the weighted wheels again takes place, and, the rear cylinder vent closing and the forward port opening, steam again drives the piston back, thus continuously turning the wheels.

The steam locomotive has held its own in the face of a growing use of electric and Diesel engines and of increasing competition by airplanes, trucks, and busses. The rapid application of inventions to improve service and bring out the inherent advantages of steam train travel has been, however, greatly stimulated by the outside competition. One of the best known innovations in modern locomotives is the practice of streamlining.

Streamlining principles had been in operation in the design of European trains for many years before they were adopted by American locomotive designers. American locomotives had possessed a complex external maze of pipes, tubes, valves, domes, driving and connecting rods, cylinders and other projecting surfaces which made the engine an impressive but hardly beautiful sight.

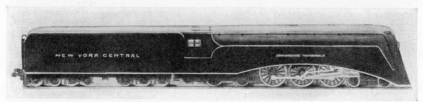

Courtesy Timken Roller Bearing Co.

THE "COMMODORE VANDERBILT"
The world's first streamlined, high-powered steam locomotive.

Courtesy Baltimore and Ohio R.R.

THE OLD AND THE NEW

A new streamlined train, the "Royal Blue," photographed on the Thomas Viaduct at Relay
House, Md., built in 1835.

Courtesy Baltimore and Ohio R.R.

THE STEAM LOCOMOTIVE OF THE FUTURE

The constant-torque locomotive, with specifications calling for sixteen cylinders and the power to handle fourteen Pullman cars at a sustained speed of 100 miles an hour.

The action of these projecting surfaces in increasing air resistance is obvious, although for many years it was not apparently so, and railroad shops vied in producing complicated and yet more complicated engine hulls. With the necessity of reducing running time, the railroads discovered that by eliminating needless air resistance they could achieve significant increases in speed. Streamlining has added to both the aesthetic attractiveness and the operating efficiency of the modern locomotive.

Other inventions have improved the actual operating principles of steam locomotion. One of the most striking modern changes in the application of steam is the "constant torque" locomotive. In this radical departure each axle is driven by four directly geared cylinders, two for each wheel. There are no heavy driving or connecting rods slung on the sides, the thrust of the cylinders and pistons being applied directly to the wheels. This design eliminates the pounding slash of the counterbalances and rods, lessening discomfort for the passengers as well as wear and tear on the road bed and rails. In operation the sixteen cylinders produce a smooth and continuous flow of power, similar to that of an automobile. Still more radical steps in the direction of more efficient high-speed transportation are propeller-driven streamliners and motorized ball bearings for wheels, used experimentally by M. I. Yarmolchuk in Russia.

IN THE EARLY DAYS of railroading there were no brakes of any sort. On the first crude locomotives projecting spikes were sometimes fitted to the rim of the wheels to give increased "adhesion." This was sufficient to overcome the force of gravity on slight grades of the primitive railways, whereas on a level track the internal resistance was nearly equal to the impelling force. When, however, the locomotive became "too smart in its movements" by reduction of internal friction, there arose an urgent necessity for some means of stopping it. This led to the use of a hand brake similar to that used on carriages and wagons, and later a steam brake, invented by Robert Stephenson in 1843. A railroad historian in speaking of this said: "When the steam brake was put on, the folks were unpleasantly jostled together, first ahead and then back; and the concussion was not in any way adapted to induce people to patronize the lines."

Thus very early came the realization of the need for retarding, not only the locomotive, but each vehicle in the train, by means of braking resistance set up on that vehicle itself. At first this need was met by hand brakes operated on the individual cars by guards or brakemen upon receiving a signal from the engineer. When the whistle was blown, perhaps a half mile from the station, the men set the brakes on one car and then rushed to the next and repeated the operation. If they were quick and skilful, they brought the train to a stop somewhere near the station. There was nothing accurate about the method and nothing safe. Accidents were frequent, and taken as a matter of course, until one day the effects of a head-on collision set a wide-awake young man to thinking of railroad brakes. Two freight trains had come together on a straight level track in broad daylight. Amid this piled-up wreckage, cars and merchandise strewn along the right of way, a new idea was born. If the engineers had themselves been able to apply the brakes instead of whistling for them the results would unquestionably have been vastly different. But how could the engineers be given control of the train brakes? Continuous mechanical connections were too cumbersome, and with steam connections too much power was lost in transmission.

It is true that various forms of brake were proposed, tried, and a few regularly operated. Among these were chain brakes, spring brakes, hydraulic brakes, buffer brakes, etc., the common object of these being to place in the hands of the engineer a means for the safe, certain, and flexible control of retarding and stopping trains, just as command of the locomotive engine gave him control of the accelerating and running of his train.

WESTINGHOUSE'S CHANCE DISCOVERY

The answer to all this came suddenly and unexpectedly, through a chance reading of an article reporting that compressed air had been piped three thousand feet into a mountain and there used to drill holes in solid rock. "Why can't it be piped throughout a train and be made to apply the brakes on each car? It can be and will be!" said this young enthusiast, George Westinghouse, the son of a mechanic and inventor. Thus the air brake came, not in its perfected form of course, but the idea itself had germinated. A patent was granted in 1868 to Westinghouse for his first air brake. He had already invented a number of mechanical devices, including a rotary steam engine.

This first air brake was a simple equipment comprising a steam-driven air compressor mounted on the locomotive; an air storage reservoir; a three-way valve in the engine cab; a pipe running throughout the train, joined by hose and couplings between cars; and a brake cylinder on each car. By means of the three-way cock the engineer admitted air to the train pipe and car cylinders for applying the brakes (forcing shoes against the wheels through rods and levers), and exhausting air to the atmosphere for releasing the brakes. This arrangement of devices became known as the "Straight Air Brake."

GEORGE WESTINGHOUSE

Inventor of the air brake, and one of America's great inventors and industrialists. Mr. Westinghouse is standing in the center; with him are Rear Admiral George Melville, U. S. N., and John H. MacAlpine, inventor.

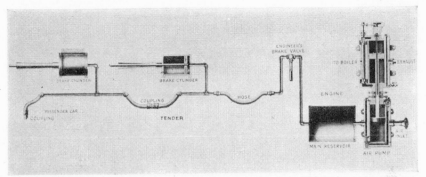

Courtesy Westinghouse Air Brake Co

THE STRAIGHT AIR BRAKE
A diagram of the first air brake developed by George Westinghouse in 1868.

Westinghouse had considerable difficulty in gaining favorable attention for his invention. Even his own father considered the idea too visionary to warrant his support, and railroad men were at first skeptical of its practicability. By fortunate chance he met a young man near his own age, Ralph Baggaley, a member of a wealthy family of Pittsburgh. This chance acquaintanceship ripened into friendship and co-operative effort, Westinghouse supplying the idea, Baggaley the money. With finances thus provided, the first air brake was built. Finally, through the combined efforts of the two young enthusiasts, several prominent railroad men became actively interested in the new brake. They arranged for its application to a locomotive and four cars comprising a local train running out of Pittsburgh.

Many prominent railroad men rode this train on its first trip, to witness a demonstration of the brake's effectiveness. They were surprised and thoroughly convinced by an unexpected test even before the train emerged from the city limits— an impending collision with a horse-drawn vehicle was narrowly averted. Other demonstrations of more pretentious extent, which soon followed, proved conclusively that trains could successfully be controlled by brakes operated with compressed air, and many railroads began to apply them to their passenger trains. Within a period of five years more than 2,000 locomotives and 7,000 cars had been equipped, which was noteworthy progress for that period of railroad transportation.

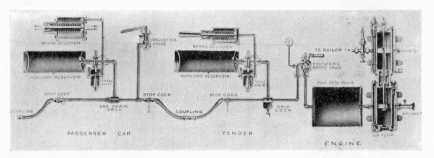

Courtesy Westinghouse Air Brake Co.

THE PLAIN AUTOMATIC AIR BRAKE OF 1872

FROM STRAIGHT TO AUTOMATIC

It soon became evident, however, to Westinghouse and others, that the "Straight Air Brake" had shortcomings making it unsuitable for trains of any considerable length on account of the time required to apply and release and the unequal braking effect throughout the train. More important was the fact that if the hose between cars accidentally uncoupled there was no brake available. The young inventor, still in his early twenties, realized that with an effective brake an accident occurring in the system should result in application rather than loss of the brake. With characteristic resourcefulness, he undertook to correct the shortcoming, and in 1872 invented and introduced the "Automatic Air Brake." This involved the use of an "auxiliary reservoir," and a "triple valve" on each car. The train line and reservoir were normally kept charged. To make an application the engineer reduced train line pressure, which caused the triple valve to operate and admit air from the reservoir to the brake cylinder. To release the brake, pressure was restored in the train line and the triple valve then operated to exhaust air from the brake cylinder and permit restoration of reservoir pressure from the train line. It will be evident that, since this brake operated by a *reduction* of train line pressure, any rupture of pipe or hose, or separation of couplings, would cause a brake application.

The automatic brake has been considered the most remarkable single development ever made in the braking field, because the principle of operation that Westinghouse determined was so basically correct that it remains to this day the foundation for all amplified and refined forms of the purely pneumatic brake.

Up to the year 1880 the use of the air brake was limited to passenger trains. Its advantages here were soon so well recognized that the railroads began to appreciate its potential value for freight trains as well. It was soon realized, however, that for longer trains the automatic brake itself had a shortcoming in that when a quick application was attempted, the stopping of the train was often rough and long drawn-out. The reason for the slow operation was that the air in the train line could not be quickly and uniformly reduced throughout its entire length. This was because of increased air volume, frictional resistance, and the necessity for air to travel to one outlet, i.e. through the brake valve at the head end of the train.

QUICK ACTION TRIPLE VALVE

This limitation was overcome by another invention of Westinghouse in 1887, the "quick action" triple valve. It functioned similarly to the first triple valve for ordinary or "service" application, but for emergencies it made possible the automatic venting of air from the brake pipe locally on each car. The rapid reduction thus resulting was transmitted to the next triple valve and

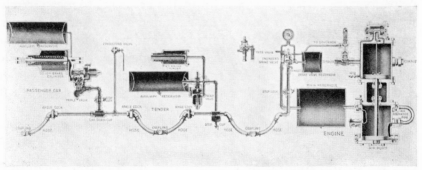

Courtesy Westinghouse Air Brake Co.

THE QUICK ACTION AUTOMATIC BRAKE
Developed in 1887, the principles used in the construction of this brake have never been altered in subsequent improvements.

from it serially in the same manner to all valves in the train, thereby reducing the time of full brake application to a fraction of that possible with the simple or "plain" triple valve, as it was later called. Shocks were correspondingly reduced in frequency and intensity, and the stopping distance shortened. A further advantage was realized in that with one form of the quick action device the local venting of air was into the brake cylinder. This provided a somewhat higher retarding force for emergencies than that obtained from service applications, which was not possible with the original "plain" triple valve. The equipment with which this new valve was used became known as the "Quick Action Automatic Brake."

It is a remarkable fact that through all subsequent improvements not one of the original functions of the triple valve has been discarded, but they have been extended and expanded, and many new functions added as conditions required, throughout the many stages of railway progress. The air-brake equipments of today are therefore more complex and varied than the early types.

MORE THAN SAFETY

Safety was the chief function of the air brake in the early days, a means to prevent accidents. Although still a safety device of paramount importance, this invention has come to mean much more than that. Then trains were light and speeds low. Now we have heavy tonnage freights a mile long, and palatial all-steel passenger trains. Efficient air-brake control permits these trains to travel at economy-promoting speeds in perfect safety. No other device has played a more important part in the advancement of steam railroads than the air brake. Moreover, its influence has extended to other fields of transportation.

Running on our city streets years ago was the small trolley car, which was stopped by a slow-acting hand brake. The clattering streetcar has evolved into a swiftly moving streamlined coach that can be stopped in a hurry—with air brakes. Fast schedules are maintained in safety.

Subway and elevated trains in large municipal centers must render fast and frequent service. They are stopped quickly and accurately with the most highly refined electro-pneumatic brake, that assures reliable mass transportation.

Highway transportation also is being helped to attain its rightful place in the commercial world by better brakes. It has been given an impetus by air brakes during the last decade just as the railroads have for almost seventy years and the street railways for almost forty years.

INVENTOR OF THE PULLMAN

A S THE early western railroads extended their lines, and distances between runs became greater, passengers demanded overnight sleeping accommodations. The Cumberland Valley Railroad of Pennsylvania was the first to meet this demand in their train service between Harrisburg and Chambersburg in 1836. Their sleeping car was primitive indeed! Springless bunks with thin mattresses were fitted into compartments along the side of a day coach. A tin washbasin and a community towel at the rear of the car gave the weary traveler his only chance to freshen himself after a bumpy and usually sleepless night. Since bedding was not provided, no one undressed, and coats and shawls were much in demand for covers.

In the early fifties, a young moving contractor, George M. Pullman, spent many uncomfortable nights in one of these sleeping cars on his trips between Westfield and Buffalo, New York. He had obtained a contract to move some structures that blocked the widening of the Erie Canal. On one of these business journeys the thought came to him, "Why not build a convertible car, which can be used as a day coach and a sleeper—with real mattresses, bedding, and attractive furnishings?"

When he finished his moving operations, he had $6,000 profit, and with that as capital this energetic and restless youth of twenty-four determined in 1855 to try his fortune in the booming, fast growing town of Chicago. There again he was able to use his engineering knowledge, for Chicago was built on such swampy ground that it became necessary to raise the whole business district from ten to fifteen feet. Pullman soon had contracts to raise a number of buildings and streets. One of these structures was the famous Tremont House. He guaranteed to hoist the hotel so efficiently that the guests would not lose any meals or sleep. He kept his promise, and succeeded so well in other ventures that his little fortune grew to $20,000 by 1858.

GEORGE M. PULLMAN
Builder of the first Pullman car, and founder of the
company that bears his name.

SLEEPER NO. 9

During these years in the West, he did not forget his idea of
constructing a sleeping car. He bought two coaches from the
Chicago and Alton road and remodeled them into sleepers at a
cost of $1,000 apiece, the first being the historic No. 9.

In Bloomington, September 1, 1859, few passengers noticed
anything different about the Chicago-bound train. Yet several
very adventurous souls entered the rear car on which were painted
the words, "Sleeping Car 9." On the platform stood an excited
and nervous young man who frequently walked through the new
coach—he was the builder and owner, George Pullman.

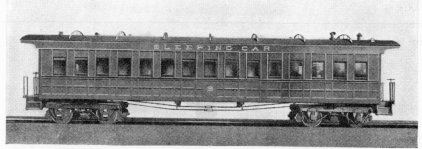

Courtesy The Pullman Co.

NO. 9, THE FIRST SLEEPING CAR
Built by George M. Pullman in 1859 at Bloomington, Ill.

As the train left Bloomington and the passengers got ready for bed, the conductor had to ask them to take off their boots before entering their berths; all but Pullman feared to remove them.

Those who are curious may still see the famous No. 9 when they visit Chicago, for it stands in honorable retirement in the Calumet Shop, adjoining the Pullman Car Works. This interesting old wooden coach was an attraction at the Chicago Century of Progress Exposition. Observers were fascinated by its hard plush seats, its candleholders, its low ceiling (fatal to high silk hats), its wood-burning stoves at either end, its tiny toilet compartments, its open washroom with tin basin and water tank, and its ornate cherry woodwork. You no doubt chuckled as you looked at the clumsy upper berths, suspended from the ceiling by ropes and pulleys, and were glad you did not have to sleep in one.

The guide told you that the car was divided by curtains into ten sections, which formed ten upper and ten lower berths. He graciously demonstrated how the low-back seats dropped down to form the bed, over which a thin mattress and a blanket were spread, explaining that sheets were not considered travel necessities until later.

Yet primitive and crude as No. 9 was, it did contain the idea for the folding upper berth, and was the most luxurious sleeping car in the United States in 1860. Lincoln and many other notables rode in it, but, just as the general public was accepting the new sleeping coach, the Civil War broke out. Sleepers were taken off by the government to facilitate the movement of troops and munitions.

Courtesy The Pullman Co.

INTERIOR VIEW OF NO. 9
Lincoln and many other notables rode in this first sleeping car. Note the upper berth ready for occupancy.

THE PIONEER

Pullman, wishing to improve No. 9, continued experimenting with plans and designs for sleeping cars, and built the *Pioneer*, in 1864, at a cost of $20,000. This elegant and luxurious coach may be called the first modern Pullman. Longer, wider, higher, beautifully upholstered and decorated, plate-glass windows, Brussels carpets, French mirrors, drawing rooms and sections, complete lavatories, downy mattresses, clean blankets and linen—all combined to make it the last word in travel luxury and comfort.

Railroad officials were genuinely interested, but still skeptical about the great cost of such a coach. Some of them had grudgingly spent $5,000 on sleeping cars for their own lines, and looked with utter amazement on this $20,000 creation. One of the chief problems was that the *Pioneer* was too wide for station platforms and too high for bridges. Railroad companies refused to change this equipment, and Pullman felt that his new coach was doomed to failure. Then by a queer stroke of fate, his fortunes turned.

After Lincoln's tragic death in April, 1865, his body was returned to Springfield, Illinois, via Chicago from Washington. The state of Illinois, wishing to pay the martyred President singular deference, hired the *Pioneer* for the funeral cortege from Chicago to Springfield. Hence, platforms and bridges were immediately rebuilt, and the *Pioneer* received its dedication on this sorrowful mission.

Celebrated overnight, Pullman's luxurious sleeper was placed in service at once on the Alton road, and before long other railroad companies altered their equipment so the new sleeper could run on their lines. Shortly after, General Grant further popularized the *Pioneer* by using it to travel from Detroit to his home in Galena, Illinois.

Some rail officials feared even yet that the public would not pay the extra Pullman rate, and would still demand the old sleepers. But their worries vanished as people grumbled when the Pullman berths were sold out and refused to use the cheaper sleeping cars. Passengers began to demand the comfort of traveling long distances on the same Pullman sleeper; and with this came a standardization of railroad equipment, construction and management, beneficial to both traveler and railroad company.

PALACE CAR COMPANY FORMED

In order to finance the construction of his new car, Pullman organized the Palace Car Company in 1867, and soon had forty-seven coaches in operation. By this time, he had introduced the system of employing Negro porters and a sleeping-car crew, which has remained a part of the distinctive Pullman service ever since.

European interest developed also, and in 1873 the Midland Railroad of England ordered some Pullman coaches. Soon an English branch of the company was established, and it began to build sleeping coaches for the Continent. One ambitious rail project gave Europeans Pullman service from the English Channel to the southern tip of Italy.

As the runs became increasingly longer, it became necessary to serve meals on the train. Pullman pioneered in this respect also, and built a kitchen in one end of the sleeper. To meet this demand better, he introduced the modern dining-car service in 1868. Full-course meals were served at a cost of a dollar each in hotel-style luxury. Parlor, lounge, observation, and smoking cars were Pullman contributions, but all came much later.

Repeated complaints of travelers who feared to walk through the open passageway between the sleeper and diner caused the Pullman Company to experiment in 1887 with a closed anti-telescoping vestibule. This proved useful, not only in keeping out drafts and dust, but also as an invaluable safety device in case of wrecks.

Litigation over patents and the competition of the Wagner Sleeping Car Company from 1870 to 1890, caused the Pullman Palace Car Company some dramatic and uncomfortable experiences. At one time, the New York Central gave the Wagner Company a coveted exclusive contract for service into New York City. Pullman, much aroused over losing access to that important point, hastened there to confer with Jay Gould, who controlled the Erie Railroad. This line did not extend to Chicago, but Pullman planned to connect it with other roads to give through service. The difficulty lay in the fact that the Erie cars ran on a six-foot gauge, while the two connecting lines had a standard

FOLDING BED
AIR OUTLET
WARDROBE
WASHSTAND
SLIDING DOOR

Courtesy The Pullman Co.

DIAGRAMMATIC VIEW OF THE INTERIOR OF A ROOMETTE, A NEWLY
DESIGNED TYPE OF SLEEPING CAR

gauge. Undaunted, Pullman decided to change the wheels and
their iron framework on each sleeping car where the two gauges
met. This was done so efficiently that passengers were scarcely
aware of it. This new Chicago-New York route became very
popular and profitable as well.

It was not until 1899 that the Pullman Company obtained a
virtual monopoly of the construction of sleeping cars, when it
absorbed its rival, the Wagner Sleeping Car Company. Almost
twenty years earlier Mr. Pullman had determined to build the
modern industrial center of Pullman, south of Chicago. On a
tract of 3,600 acres, a model manufacturing plant and city were

Courtesy The Pullman Co.

INTERIOR OF THE OBSERVATION SECTION OF THE NEW
TWO-CAR PULLMAN UNIT

scientifically designed and laid out with paved streets, water, lights, and sewers. Schools, homes, library, hotel, and theaters were also included in the project. This community was annexed to Chicago in 1889 and was the scene of the famous Pullman strike in 1894, in which President Cleveland intervened.

PULLMAN'S CONTRIBUTION TO LAND TRAVEL

One of Pullman's contributions to the railroad industry, frequently overlooked, was the impetus the use of his coach gave to competing lines in unifying their operations to give passengers long-distance service. The modern trend to rail combination and consolidation was but the next logical step.

The new steamlined, alloy-steel Pullmans, with their beautifully furnished private compartments, drawing rooms, and the new "roomettes;" their scientific air conditioning, modernistic decorations and fittings; their convenient washrooms; their barber shop, library, stenographic and radio service; and their efficiently trained porters, stewards and hostesses, are indeed a far cry from No. 9, with its meager furnishings and comforts.

Thus it is not without significance that the name "Pullman" is listed in the dictionaries of twenty languages as a synonym for travel comfort, safety, and luxury.

Courtesy The Pullman Co.

THE NEW LIGHT-WEIGHT, STREAMLINED TWO-CAR UNIT PUT INTO
SERVICE IN WESTERN UNITED STATES

EARLY HISTORY OF THE STEAMBOAT

T HOUSANDS OF years ago, the ancient Egyptians and
Romans used boats driven by a paddle or propeller, very
similar in principle to the famous side-wheelers which
churned up and down the Mississippi before and after the Civil
War. The essential difference was in the utilization of man-power
to turn the paddles in ancient times, while in the nineteenth century steam-power was used. At first paddles simply supplemented
the motive power of the oar and sail; but, as time went on, inventive minds began to experiment with mechanical devices which
would turn the crude propellers.

A Spaniard named Blasco de Garay is credited by some with
having been the first to operate a vessel by steam, an event which
is supposed to have occurred near Barcelona in 1543. The French
maintain that a century and a half later Denis Papin was the first
to achieve this honor.

An Englishman, Jonathan Hull, patented a crude steamboat
in 1736, but could find no one to finance his invention. Perhaps
the most successful eighteenth-century experimenter was the
Frenchman, Marquis de Jouffroy, who utilized Papin's theories,
and built a successful steamboat in 1780. Unfortunately, Jouffroy's work was cut short by the French Revolution.

JOHN FITCH, AMERICAN INVENTOR OF
THE STEAMBOAT

At about the same time, John Fitch, a native of Connecticut
and an itinerant clock and gun repairer, had just returned from
an exciting trading venture in the Ohio country. Captured by
the Indians at the mouth of the Muskingum River, he was forced
to go on foot to Lake Erie. He finally escaped and reached War-

minster, Pennsylvania, in 1785, where he immediately began experimenting with a steamboat which could be used on the western rivers. Fitch was thoroughly convinced that the future of the United States depended on the development of the transportation and communication facilities in the West.

His tragic failure to establish himself as the American inventor of the steamboat, was not due to any lack of inventive genius or engineering skill on his part, but to a lack of financial backing. In many interviews with the members of the Continental Congress, state legislators, and scientific leaders he met only with rebuff and discouragement.

Fitch constructed a small steamboat driven by side propellers, and demonstrated it successfully on the Schuylkill River. After this triumph he succeeded in getting monopoly rights to operate his boats on the waters of New York, New Jersey, Pennsylvania, Delaware, and Virginia for a period of fourteen years. At this time a few Philadelphians did organize a company to aid his experiments, but never furnished sufficient capital or moral backing to be of substantial service to him.

In 1787 Fitch designed a boat fitted out with paddles, which operated in the same fashion as an Indian canoe. On a trial run on the Delaware River before a curious crowd, including members of the Continental Congress, this crude vessel maintained a speed of four miles an hour for forty miles. An improved boat, built by him the next year, doubled this speed, and in 1790 his third vessel maintained a regular passenger and freight schedule between Philadelphia and Burlington, New Jersey.

This last project caused some favorable comment, but even yet the steamboat was looked upon as a freak invention. People feared to ride on it, and shippers were dubious of entrusting valuable cargoes to such a strange craft. Fitch started to build a fourth boat, only to have it destroyed by a storm before it was completed. By this time his few backers were utterly disgusted and refused to risk any more funds on the luckless inventor.

Thoroughly discouraged in 1793, he finally decided to sail for France to try his fortune there. Although he succeeded in patenting his steamboat, construction plans were ended with the outbreak of the French Revolution. Before leaving Paris, Fitch turned over his patent drawings to the American Consul, who gave them to Robert Fulton, a young American artist and engineer, then in the French capital.

Fitch returned to the United States, and in 1796, while in New York, made one final attempt to arouse an interest in his steamboat. Although his screw-propeller craft worked successfully, the public was still not ready to accept his invention. Fitch retired to his Kentucky holdings nears Bardstown, where, two years later, he took his own life in a moment of despondency. His grave in the public square of Bardstown is marked with only a marble shaft, but the modern world now places him first among American inventors and experimenters with the steamboat. It was his misfortune to introduce his invention too soon, and the honor and acclaim that might have been his went to Robert Fulton.

ROBERT FULTON

JOHN STEVENS—MANUFACTURER OF STEAMBOATS

Among the interested spectators watching the trial runs of John Fitch's boat on the Delaware was Colonel John Stevens of New York City. Believing that steamboats had a great future, he determined to manufacture them. The discomforts and difficulties he experienced in rowing or sailing across the Hudson to his New Jersey country home were added inducements to build a faster and safer means of transportation.

Stevens had an uncanny faculty for seeing flaws in the inventions of others, and fortunately had sufficient means to perfect his improvements in the steamboat. In 1798 he successfully operated a steam vessel on the Hudson, nearly ten years before Fulton. Constantly improving his factory, he became the best steamboat builder in America, but was still hampered by the lack of tools and a determination to use only American products. His most important contribution to the steamboat, however, was the improvement of the screw propeller. In 1807, he constructed the *Phoenix*, which he was forced to send to Philadelphia to operate, because of Fulton's monopoly rights on the Hudson. This vessel was the first steam-driven craft to venture on the ocean, but attracted very little attention because of the more publicized feat of Fulton's *Clermont* the previous year.

Stevens' son, Robert L. Stevens, also made significant contributions in the same field. His introduction of the false bow increased the speed of the steamboat materially, while his designs for ferryboats, river craft, and ferry berths are still used.

ROBERT FULTON AND THE DEVELOPMENT OF THE STEAMBOAT

Robert Fulton's importance lies largely in the fact that he was ingenious enough to adopt and incorporate the latest improvements in his own steamboat experiments, and was the first to make steam navigation commercially successful. Fulton was born in Pennsylvania in 1765. As a child he excelled in drawing, and displayed much inventive genius. The story is told that he became interested in the steamboat at the age of fourteen, when, to escape the hard work of rowing or poling on his fishing trips, he built a paddle wheel which could be turned by hand.

The stern necessity of earning a living cut short his inventive attempts for a number of years, and he turned to his painting and drawing to support himself in Philadelphia. His art work had attracted the attention of the painter, Benjamin West, a former friend and neighbor, then living in London. At his suggestion, Fulton went to England where he became absorbed in the new scientific and mechanical era development on that island.

While taking a trip through the southwestern part of England, Fulton met the Duke of Bridgewater and the Earl of Stanhope, both of whom were canal engineers and inventors. Canal building interested Fulton so much that he spent the next six years experimenting with problems of canal engineering, and soon became a leading authority in that field.

When the canal projects failed to be as profitable as he expected, he turned his attention to building a submarine with a torpedo attachment. He went to France and succeeded in interesting the French government in his unusual invention, whose trial in the Seine in 1800 was astonishingly successful. After much urging, Fulton got the French officials to promise a large sum for every English ship he could sink with his submarine. He navigated his queer craft for seventy miles, trying to sink English vessels, but they were able to avoid him, having been warned of Fulton's plans.

During the course of his experiments, he became acquainted with the new American minister to France, Robert Livingston, who had secured the Fitch monopoly of New York waters, but as yet had not been able to build a practical steamboat. He had not lost his interest in steam navigation, however, and formed a partnership with Fulton. The latter agreed to build a steam vessel which could operate on the Hudson at a speed of eight miles per hour while carrying sixty passengers. First this enterprising American built a steamboat in France but before its trial the heavy machinery crashed through the hull and sank in the river Seine. Fulton rescued it and installed the engine in another vessel which,

Courtesy Chicago Historical Society

THE *CLERMONT*

to his great satisfaction, proved successful in its first trial, although it moved very slowly.

He determined to go back to England in 1804 and study plans of English boats and steam engines, being particularly interested in William Symington's vessel, *Charlotte Dundas*, which had been operating successfully since 1802 on the Forth and Clyde canal. Symington reluctantly gave the American inventor permission to make drawings of his machinery. Believing that the Boulton and Watt engine was the best built, Fulton finally made arrangements to take one with him when he returned to the United States in 1806.

The construction of his famous boat, the *Clermont*, began in New York the same year under his personal supervision. By the first of August, 1807, the English-built engine was installed and the vessel was ready for operation. One newspaper writer pictured it an "an ungainly craft looking precisely like a backwoods sawmill mounted on a scow and set on fire." After a successful preliminary trial run on August 7 with the *Clermont*, nicknamed "Fulton's Folly" by a jeering, scornful public, Fulton made ready for the historic trip up the Hudson River.

Ten days later the new vessel left New York for Albany with forty persons on board, including, of course, the excited promoter. A motley crowd of curious spectators stood on the riverbank, a few were hopeful, but it was evident that the majority were there to watch the failure of this newest freak steamboat. Instead, however, "Fulton's Folly" steamed up the river to Albany, a distance of one hundred and fifty miles in thirty-two hours, and made a return trip in two hours less, at an average speed of five miles an hour in both cases.

Public opinion completely changed after the *Clermont's* successful runs. Realizing this, Fulton made improvements on his boat, building enclosed cabins, a kitchen, a dining-room, and perfecting the machinery. Soon the original investment of twenty thousand dollars was paying a five per cent return. Fulton and his backers added two boats to their line, and before long New York and Albany had daily steamer service. Ferries were built to operate between New York and New Jersey on half-hour schedules; they could carry one hundred passengers, eight vehicles and thirty horses.

The War of 1812 and law suits over water rights interfered with Fulton's plans, but his company did succeed in establishing a line of steamers to Providence, Rhode Island. It was not until 1824, however, when the Supreme Court declared the navigable waters of the United States opened to everyone, that steamboat service became general.

At the time of his death in 1815 Fulton was building a steam warship for the government. Unfortunately, he did not live to see its completion. His chief contribution to the world lies in the fact that he was the first man who had sufficient patience, courage, and vision to make the steamboat a commercial success. His role in society and his claim to fame are just as great as that of Fitch, the real American inventor. It took the combined effort and genius of each of these men to give the world what it had long been awaiting—a profitable and fast means of water transportation.

STEAMBOATS ON THE WESTERN RIVERS AND LAKES

While Fulton was operating his boats in the East, Nicholas J. Roosevelt, a former partner of John Stevens, and a builder of steam engines, was constructing the *New Orleans* at Pittsburgh. This river steamboat was launched in 1811 amidst much excitement. Few doubted that the *New Orleans* could go down stream, for even a barge could do that! But the real test lay in its ability to move upstream. Fortunately for Roosevelt and his backers, the new vessel met this last test successfully.

Steamboats appeared shortly on all the western rivers, and opened a colorful and glamorous era, soon celebrated in story and song. As mechanical improvements and size of the boats increased, rival captains indulged in thrilling races. When fuel gave out, cargoes, hams, tar, or almost anything at hand fed the voracious furnaces. Frequently the over-heated boilers exploded, scalding both crew and passengers; while fires often resulted in tragic

Courtesy International Harvester Co.

AN ORE FREIGHTER
Heavy, specialized traffic in ore on the Great Lakes has resulted in the development of great steam freighters such as this, which carries iron ore from Duluth-Superior to the blast furnaces at Chicago and other industrial centers.

drownings and loss of ship and cargo. The railroads took over most of this picturesque traffic, although in recent years oil-burning barges have recaptured some of the mid-west freight trade.

The steamboat was launched on the Great Lakes about the same time as it was on the western rivers. The first successful Great Lakes steam vessel, the *Walk-in-the-water*, began operating in 1818 on Lake Erie. Traffic on the Great Lakes was stimulated first by the lumber industry, and much later by the discovery of rich copper and iron deposits in northern Michigan and Minnesota. As the agricultural West developed, much grain went to eastern markets from the inland ports of Duluth and Superior, while they in turn became the western distributing centers for automobiles, hardware, furniture, and various other manufactured products from the East.

Today the cargoes of ore and grain are carried in boats which are improvements on the old whaleback. They are loaded by mechanical devices in about two hours, and unloaded with equal ease at the smelter or elevator dock by huge grab-buckets, each depositing from five to fifteen tons. Although the Great Lakes are ice-bound in the winter months, the summer traffic has increased by leaps and bounds.

THE STEAMBOAT ON THE HIGH SEAS

The first steam-powered vessel to cross the Atlantic was the *Savannah*, which crossed from Savannah, Georgia, to Liverpool in twenty-seven days in 1819. Her steam engines were used for only eighty hours of the trip, due to a lack of wood and coal. A humorist of the day proposed that each steamship be convoyed by a fueling fleet. The *Savannah*'s return voyage via Stockholm and St. Petersburg stimulated great interest on the Continent. British shippers and ship builders hastened to meet American competition. The *Conde de Patmella*, an English-built steamer, began operating between England and Brazil in 1820, and the world's first steamship company, the General Steam Navigation Company, was established in London the same year.

Steam was slow to take the place of the sail, for the engine boilers were not well constructed and frequently exploded with disastrous consequences, and fires from overheated furnaces were a constant menace to the wooden ships. By the forties some improvement had occurred in steamship building, boilers were stronger, and some safety devices were adopted; while the introduction of an improved screw propeller greatly increased the speed and efficiency of the engine.

ERICSSON—BUILDER OF THE MONITOR

Captain John Ericsson, a Swedish marine engineer living in England, was among those who successfully experimented with the screw propeller. Captain R. H. Stockton, of the United States Navy, was so impressed with Ericsson's invention that he contracted with him to build a small iron vessel for the government.

The Swedish inventor thereupon came to New York City and began to construct iron-clad vessels. During the Civil War, the Navy Department engaged him to build an armored vessel. This unique craft, named the *Monitor,* and known as the "Yankee cheesebox on a raft," was launched on January 30, 1862, and had the famous conflict with its southern iron-clad rival, the *Merrimac*, six weeks later. Although this naval battle was not a decisive one, it did prove to the world that wooden warships were no longer practical, and, from that time on, iron and steel gradually took the place of wood in all battleship construction.

By 1870 the era of the sailing vessel was passing, although one might still see in New England harbors graceful clipper ships just returned from Chinese or other Far Eastern ports with their holds filled with silks, tea, lacquered ware, and spices.

THE MODERN LINER

The huge, luxurious, and fast modern liners are vastly different from the first unsafe and inefficient steamboats. Enterprising companies, since Fulton's day, have been constantly on the alert to improve their boats and service.

Courtesy North German Lloyd Lines

THE S. S. EUROPA
Luxury liner which once held the record for the fastest North Atlantic crossing.

Courtesy Museum of Science and Industry, Chicago

MODEL DEMONSTRATING WAY A SHIP'S GYRO STABILIZER FUNCTIONS
This device has been installed on only one great passenger liner, the Conte di Savoia.

With the establishment of the famous Cunard Line in 1840, and other successful steamship companies shortly after, England dominated the transoceanic shipping business. The United States government, in an attempt to build up American business, subsidized the Collins Lines. This company constructed fine vessels, luxuriously appointed, even including the innovation of steam heat in the cabins. A series of financial misfortunes and sea disasters, however, resulted in the government withdrawing its aid, and English supremacy remaining secure.

By the middle of the nineteenth century, the length of the larger steamships increased to nearly five hundred feet. England startled the shipping world in 1854 with the *Great Western*, six hundred seventy-nine feet long and eighty-two feet wide. In fact, her proportions were not equaled by any vessel for over fifty years. The development of the compound engine, improved boilers, and the introduction of twin-screw propellers and steel hulls produced a great increase in the efficiency and the extent of world shipping operations. The present size, luxurious appointments, and speed of the passenger ships had their origin in the introduction in 1870 of the White Star liner, *Oceanic*, which crossed the Atlantic in eight days.

The entrance of Germany into the shipbuilding competition toward the end of the century gave England a real race for supremacy. The Hamburg-American and North German Lloyd liners, the *Kaiser Wilhelm der Grosse* and the *Deutschland* lowered the English crossing records. The Cunard Line immediately began building even larger vessels, and with the *Lusitania* and *Mauretania* regained her coveted rank.

Continued improvements in safety devices, such as the gyroscopic compass, and wireless equipment, have made sea disasters infrequent. Since the invention of the oil-burning Diesel engine, many shipbuilders have used it with varying results, although most engineers agree that it has great possibilities. A great many of the larger liners, such as the *Queen Mary*, have adopted the oil-burning turbo-electric engine.

Courtesy Cunard-White Star Line

TOURIST CLASS DINING SALON OF THE LARGEST THING AFLOAT,
THE "QUEEN MARY"

THE MODERN PASSENGER SHIP

The *Roma, Rex,* and gyro-stabilized *Conte di Savoia,* the *Normandie, Ile de France, Europa, Bremen, Empress of Canada,* the *Queen Mary* (the world's largest vessel), *Manhattan,* and the *Washington,* are all excellent examples of the modern floating palace. Even to attempt to list the luxurious appointments and equipment on these costly liners would be an endless task. The more outstanding conveniences include beautifully furnished cabins, spacious decks, swimming pools, libraries, recreation rooms for children and adults, daily newspapers, smart shops, excellent orchestras, and world-wide radio and telephone service.

Perhaps it might be interesting to give a few statistics on the British liner, *Queen Mary.* She can carry 2,075 passengers, and contains three acres of deck space for recreation, equal to the ground area of the Yale Bowl. Her rudder weighs one hundred and sixty tons, or equal to the total tonnage of the *Mayflower.* The refrigeration plant of the steamer totals sixty thousand cubic feet, or enough refrigeration for fifteen thousand homes; while seven turbo-generators deliver enough electrical energy to meet the electrical needs of a city of one hundred and fifty thousand people, such as San Diego, Tulsa, or Spokane.

THE MODERN WARSHIP

Our discussion of the steamboat would be incomplete without sketching briefly the history of the modern fighting ship. It was not until 1850 that steam took the place of sails in the navies of the world, or that the iron-clad and steel hull took the place of wooden framework. As has previously been mentioned, the *Merrimac-Monitor* encounter in the Civil War convinced naval experts that the wooden warship was obsolete.

From that time on, battleship construction progressed at a terrific pace in every country. Not only did naval authorities adopt all the mechanical and technical improvements which were incorporated in the passenger and freight steamers, but greatly increased the effectiveness of the various types of guns and other

Courtesy Jacksonville, Fla., Chamber of Commerce
A U. S. DESTROYER IN JACKSONVILLE HARBOR

defensive equipment. This process went on continuously, and the efforts of engineers were directed to the construction of ships of the swift cruiser type, instead of the large battleship.

It was not until 1883 that the United States began to construct the modern armored vessel. In 1890 Congress let a contract for the building of three first-class warships, the *Oregon*, the *Indiana*, and the *Massachusetts*. Sentiment for a larger naval defense grew after the excellent work of the navy during the Spanish-American War.

The appearance of the dreadnaught outfitted with thick armor-plate, large turret guns, and steam turbines brought about revolutionary changes in battleship building. This type of ship costs today at least fifteen million dollars, carries a crew of over a thousand men, has from ten to twelve large guns and many smaller ones. Today these vessels burn oil to operate the steam

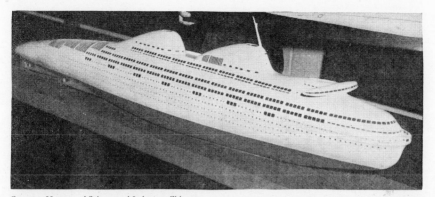

Courtesy Museum of Science and Industry, Chicago
THE SHIP OF THE FUTURE, AS VISUALIZED BY NORMAN BEL GEDDES

turbines, but in some instances turbo-electric drives are being used successfully.

The battle cruiser is lighter and hence faster than the battleship, carries fewer guns, and is protected by thinner armor plate. Other types of naval vessels include coast-defense ships, light cruisers, destroyers, aircraft carriers, torpedo boats, and submarines.

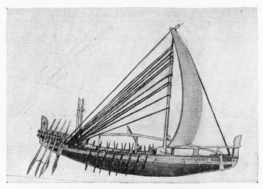

A SHIP OF THE PAST
It was in frail craft like this that ancient mariners
sailed treacherous seas.

S LEEK, streamlined trolley cars move swiftly and quietly down Madison Street in Chicago. The conductor sits comfortably in the front, operating a few levers, buttons, and pedals. Doors open as if by magic, and long breakshoes drop from the trucks to bring the car to a smooth stop. There is a long story back of the comfort, safety, and reliability of these beautiful vehicles—a story that begins with the two-wheeled cart and is as old as civilization.

Man has never been especially fond of walking long distances. Wherever possible, he has used means of transportation other than the legs which nature provided. Horses, camels, and burros; carts, chariots, and coaches—all were called into use to relieve man of the necessity of moving himself. When cities grew into sprawling communities with people living blocks and even miles from shops, offices, and factories, the problem of getting from place to place became acute. Horse-drawn carriages, "buggies," and carts were familiar sights. As early as 1662, Pascal devised an omnibus for use in Paris. Stagecoaches, prominent in travel between cities, were used for city transportation on Broadway in New York City in 1830.

The next step was not very revolutionary; it consisted of building a glorified stage on wheels to run on a track. The first horse-drawn streetcar appeared in the transportation world in 1832. The New York and Harlem Railroad, organized in 1831, opened a route that ran up Fourth Avenue to Murray Hill, now the site of Grand Central Terminal. John Stephenson built the first car, which was named the "John Mason." Running on flanged wheels over strap-rails laid on stone ties, these pioneer horse-cars were not much of a success. However, between 1850 and 1855, a half-dozen American cities were using these strange vehicles. A Frenchman, Laubey, invented a grooved track in 1852. This development produced many imprecations when wagon and carriage wheels caught in the grooves with disastrous consequences. A step-rail, which overcame this difficulty, was devised and placed in use in Philadelphia in 1855. An American, George Francis Train, introduced the horsecar to England in 1860. By that time there were about forty such streetcar systems in the United States. But when electrical power became available a few years later, street railways developed so rapidly that by 1890 more than 750 cities had them.

FROM CABLE CARS TO ELECTRIC ROADS

An interesting variation of the street railway was invented by Andrew S. Halliday in 1820, to solve the problems presented by San Francisco's steep streets. This ingenious mechanic fathered the cable car, which was not used to any extent until 1870. The cars were hauled by endless cables running in a slotted conduit between the tracks. The conductor, or gripman, operated levers

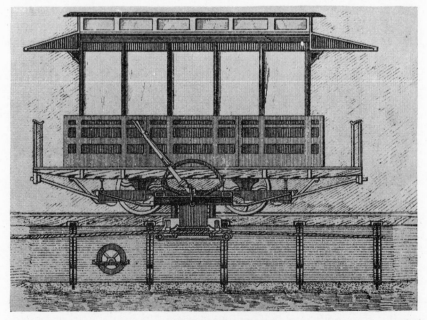

THE CABLE CAR
In hilly San Francisco, this device did its part to solve the transportation problem in 1876.

which reached down to grip the cable. Huge drums at central stations kept the cables moving. Unfortunately, if a break occurred along the line, every car was delayed to await repairs; and, if a quick stop or start became necessary because of traffic conditions, the gripman was almost helpless. Cables are still used occasionally, especially on short, scenic railways.

Even while the horsecars were increasing their vogue on city streets, visionary engineers were seeking a more satisfactory source of power. Tom Davenport, a struggling young blacksmith at Brandon, Vermont, neglected his forge to play with the fascinating electromagnet invented by Professor Joseph Henry at Albany Academy. Becoming the delighted possessor of one of these toys in 1833, Davenport saw its possibilities. By 1834 he had built a motor, which was patented three years later. The story is told that the inventor was so poor that he borrowed his wife's silk wedding dress to use for insulating the coils!

One of Davenport's inventions was the commutator to collect current from the coils that revolved rapidly in an electromagnetic field. By no means an idle dreamer, the former blacksmith built a model electric railroad. Batteries, placed in the center of the circular track, supplied the current. The Electromagnetic Association, organized by Davenport in 1837, foreshadowed the modern electric power companies. During the next few years many other experimenters worked with battery cars. Robert Davidson in Scotland, Moses Farmer and C. G. Page in the United States, all had discouraging experiences. Not until the invention of the dynamo was electric traction to be commercially successful.

THIRD RAIL

Many men are credited with developing the dynamo to generate electricity. Faraday discovered the basic principle; Henry Wilde in England made important contributions in 1863; and Z. T. Gramme in Belgium constructed an industrially successful dynamo in 1870. Three years later, Wilde exhibited his own generator at Vienna. Their achievements inspired Stephen Field, nephew of Cyrus Field of cable fame, to plan an electric railway for San Francisco which would use power delivered by a centrally located power station. Field's plans, patented in 1877, called for a dynamo to transmit current to a third rail. One of the wheels would pick up the current and deliver it to a motor. The circuit was completed by using another wheel and rail. High voltages necessary to operate a streetcar made this surface third rail dangerous. Werner Siemens in Berlin built an electric railway from Berlin to Lichterfelde in 1881 without using the third rail by putting the motor into the car.

The overhead trolley with its little wheel running along the wire was the invention of Charles J. Van Depole and John C. Henry. The former was a Belgian immigrant who became a successful business man in Detroit. The wheel was Van Depole's idea, while Henry is credited with having devised the trolley pole. These inventions, coming in the eighteen-eighties, and the use of the dynamo, gave a lasting impetus to the electric railway.

AN EARLY OVERHEAD TROLLEY CAR
Note that the wires are at the side.

Thomas A. Edison, the "wizard of Menlo Park," experimented with a small electric railroad which he built behind his laboratory. Edison used batteries which drove a motor connected by pulleys and belts to the axle of the car. He also conceived the idea of a multiple unit control, which was developed by one of his former associates.

This man was Frank Julian Sprague, an energetic and daring enterpriser. Sprague was in London in 1882 and disliked the smoky discomfort of the subway then in use. He proposed to electrify the cars, using overhead rails to carry the current. After a short connection with Edison in 1883, Sprague struck out for himself. He failed in an attempt to interest the financier, Jay Gould, in a controller for the Manhattan Elevated, and then signed an astonishing contract to build a complete electric railway for Richmond, Virginia, within ninety days. The attempt was successful, and the cars were in operation in February, 1888.

SPRAGUE'S CONTROLLER

Economy of operation was sought by running streetcars in short trains, with the front car pulling trailers. This principle, successful on elevated and subway systems, was poorly adapted to crowded city streets. Sprague invented a multiple unit controller by which the individual motors on several cars could be operated by the motorman in the front car of a train. Put into operation on the South Side Elevated of Chicago in 1897, the multiple unit was eminently successful.

The modern streetcar uses the overhead trolley pole in contact with a current-carrying wire. The power is conducted to motors mounted under the car. An insulated wheel in contact with the track completes the circuit. Trackless trolleys, or "bus" streetcars, are completely insulated from the ground because of the rubber tires used on the wheels. That explains the two trolley wires, one of which acts as the "ground" while the other carries the current. The voltage used is not high enough to cause a "jump" between the two wires. Air brakes, supplemented by emergency hand brakes, add to the safety of operation.

The electric subway and elevated trains are problems of en-

Courtesy Pennsylvania Railroad

NINETY MILES PER HOUR!
A streamlined electric locomotive built to pull seventeen cars at a speed of
over ninety miles an hour.

gineering rather than invention, and operate on essentially the same principles as the trolley car. A third rail, at the side or between the tracks, carries the current supplied by central power stations. Electrified railways, such as those entering Grand Central Terminal in New York, the Illinois Central system in Chicago, interurban lines, and the Chicago, Milwaukee, St. Paul and Pacific Railroad, simply apply electric traction on a large scale. The last named road has many miles of electrified tracks through the mountainous regions. The Pennsylvania Railroad has electrified some of its eastern lines. Future developments of electric traction in the United States are likely to appear primarily in the subways of large cities, and on the railroads. The cost of electrification is great, but electric power is cheaper than steam for hauling railroad traffic.

Electric street railways in small communities enjoyed only a brief period of prominence. By 1890 there were many such systems, and forty years later the motor bus had made great inroads on passenger traffic. Abandoned streetcar tracks may be seen in fairly large cities, mute reminders of the progress in transportation. But the genius of Davenport, Sprague, and their co-workers has not been wasted. Millions of passengers are still carried daily on electric street, subway, and elevated cars. What the future of these traction systems will be no one knows; but their importance cannot be overlooked in the development of metropolitan centers.

ALTHOUGH THERE ARE EVIDENCES extant that the Egyptians and other early civilizations made use of some vehicles allied to the modern bicycle, the few facts available are so sketchy that we cannot be sure of the nature of the contrivances or the extent to which they were used.

Before the addition of pedals to the bicycle by Ernest Michau in 1860, some use was made of two- and three-wheeled cycles which were pushed along by the feet. Without a better method of propulsion, however, such contraptions were bound to remain in the class of novelties rather than to become efficient means of personal transportation.

The bicycle, like many other machines, was slowly built up out of the contributions of many mechanically inclined artisans and inventors. After Michau had shown the advantages of plac-

A BONE-SHAKER OF 1866.
This clumsy iron bicycle was one of the first to use pedals.

[132]

A SPORT MODEL OF
THE '80s
Front wheels increased
greatly in size after the
introduction of pedals,
and the danger of
"spill" increased in pro-
portion.

THE "STAR" OF 1880
To overcome the dan-
gers of a headlong fall,
the "Star" with the seat
over the rear wheel, and
a ratchet device instead
of pedals, appeared
about 1880.

AN EARLY "SAFETY BICYCLE"
The type from which the modern two-
wheeler is descended.

ing a set of pedals on the front wheel, the real development of
the bicycle began. In order to get greater traction and speed the
size of the front wheel was constantly increased until it developed
into the "high-wheeler" so fashionable in the nineteenth century.

The modern safety bicycle, or "wheel," as it is familiarly
known, owes its greatest development to Colonel Albert A. Pope,
who patented it in 1886. Although his first bicycles were costly
as well as unwieldly, Pope not only found ways and means of re-

THOUSANDS OF PEOPLE LOOK BACK TO THE
TANDEM WITH ROMANTIC MEMORIES

THE "SOCIABLE" OF 1884 CONTAINED A HINT OF THE MOTORCYCLE
SIDECAR TO COME LATER

ducing both weight and costs, but in so doing he unknowingly contributed much toward a coming industrial era—that of the automobile. It was Pope and his competitors who found the economical methods of having various parts of the bicycle, such as the pedals, ball bearings, frames, spokes, and so on, manufactured in separate factories, often by independent companies, and assembling them in a central plant. Thus when the bicycle craze was being eclipsed by the automobile these manufacturers were able to build motor cars and apply their knowledge profitably. The early automobiles were built of the same type of tubing, their wheels had wire spokes like the bicycle and the use of the pneumatic tire made them much more efficient. In addition, many of the early automobiles bore the names of bicycle

Courtesy Monark Silver King, Inc.

TODAY'S LIGHT-WEIGHT, BALLOON-TIRED BICYCLE, THE
"SAFETY" IN FANCY DRESS

manufacturers. It should be remembered that we owe the invention of the airplane to two brothers who were in the bicycle business—Wilbur and Orville Wright.

Although the bicycle in the United States lost its popularity with adults after the advent of the automobile, it is even today an important method of transportation for the working classes of central Europe. An American visiting Europe today is amazed at the great number of bicycles in use by the adult population not only in getting to and from their daily occupations but also in their pleasure trips into the countryside. The motorized bicycle with the motor integral with the frame or added to the front or rear wheel is also widely used in Europe.

GASOLINE AND GUNPOWDER

THE STORY OF THE AUTOMOBILE is principally the story of the internal combustion engine, an engine which accomplished the remarkable feat of harnessing the mechanical power of fire. Instead of using its fuel indirectly to turn water into steam, it "put the furnace into the cylinder," so taking advantage of the expansive force of the gases that result from combustion. And it did not burn its fuel slowly, but with a swiftness rivaling that of a true explosion. In these days of nearly silent, soft-purring motors we are apt to forget that the difference between gasoline vapor and gunpowder is only one of degree; both are fast-burning substances, as distinguished from the rarer true explosives. In fact man, in using and experimenting with gunpowder, the earliest fast-burning substance generally known, was laying the foundations for the gasoline motor.

The cannon was the first machine devised to make use of terrific power. The cannon was reputedly first used in the thirteenth century by Jenghis Khan's Mongol horsemen, conquerors who rode their hardy ponies from the edge of the China Seas to the heart of Austria. As they watched the original crude wooden gun belch smoke and heave a stone into a besieged town, they may have dimly guessed that, before their very eyes, was the key to a secret that would render obsolete their razor-edged lances and barbed arrows; but they could hardly have known that that same cannon, using a different fuel and a piston instead of a projectile, would some day be running vehicles far speedier than their own ponies, vehicles that looked like gigantic, shiny black beetles, vehicles fast on their way to putting the whole world on wheels. If you had told them so, they would probably have laughed and, because it was such a good joke, given your skull a place of honor on top of one of their gruesome pyramids.

FIRST FORD CAR, 1896

In the next century the cannon was introduced into Europe, and it set a few profound men thinking of its potentialities for useful work as well as for slaughter. In 1680 Christian Huygens built a cylinder and piston, put a very small charge of gunpowder inside, and touched it off through a fuse hole. The piston moved, and the whole business didn't blow up and kill the inventor; that was as much success as the gunpowder engine ever had, and was all that was needed. It proved the principle, even though the fuel was too powerful and difficult to handle.

Courtesy Buffalo Museum of Science

THE OLDSMOBILE OF 1899

NEW AND BETTER FUEL

After Huygens the problem lapsed for a hundred years. Then John Street of England made an innovation: he substituted turpentine for gunpowder. This new fuel was much safer in that, until vaporized and mixed with air, it was slow-burning rather than fast-burning; there was no danger of its blowing up completely. Street's engine would seem very crude today. It had a sponge soaked in turpentine for a carburetor and an open flame for a spark-plug. As was to be expected, the flame was always blowing out, so an ignition cock was devised: a valve that opened with each thrust of the piston and let the inner wick be relit by one burning steadily just outside. In spite of their flaws, engines of this type were successfully used to pump water from mines.

At about the same time, the French mechanic Le Bon made a similar stationary one-cylinder motor, but one that used a mixture of illuminating gas and air for fuel. In the matter of ignition he made the prophetic innovation of the electric spark. But, because the bulky nature of its fast-burning material made it require a large storage tank, it could never have readily and successfully been put on wheels. Moreover, it was shaped like a cannon and its piston was round like a cannon ball, a detail that illustrates how the mind of man tends to hold fast to the conventional form of a machine, even when he has utterly changed its function.

Street's and Le Bon's engines were of the type called two-cycle. On each down-stroke the piston was propelled by the ex-

MODEL "B"
FORD, 1905

MODEL "K" FORD, 1906-7

pansive force of fast-burning vapors, and the waste gases escaped through a hole that the moving piston uncovered; during the up-stroke, as much fast-burning vapor was introduced into the cylinder as was possible during such a comparatively short and unfavorable time. In 1876 the German N. A. Otto, embodying principles thought out by other men, successfully built an engine that had four instead of two cycles. As in the others, the first down-stroke was due to the firing of the fast-burning mixture; the force of the up-stroke thoroughly expelled the waste gases; the second down-stroke sucked in the fuel; the second up-stroke compressed that fuel prior to the next firing. This compression of the fuel was an important innovation; using the same vapor in the same quantities, it increased its power and the efficiency of the whole engine. To keep the piston moving during the latter part of the cycle, a heavy flywheel was attached to the shaft it turned. The distance that the piston moved back and forth was cut down, and so a faster and lighter engine was made possible.

Like Le Bon, Otto first used illuminating gas, although the fuel of the future had already been on the market for twenty-five years. In 1850 was begun the distillation of petroleum into its various heavy and light constituents. Kerosene proved itself useful for lamps and stoves; its more inflammable and volatile brother gasoline was considered too dangerous for such purposes. It was generally allowed to waste. A few cans were put on sale, but no one had any idea of just what to do with it until the men who tinkered with internal combustion engines came along and discovered in it a fuel that they never discarded.

THE CAR STARTS

With the coming of gasoline, the swiftly developing four-cycle motor was ready to be put on wheels. There was nothing particularly remarkable in this notion itself. Whenever man invents a new kind of motor, he tries to use it to speed up things in general and himself in particular. The early European automobile races were entered by rocket-like contrivances propelled with jets of compressed air, by machines that wound up like clockwork—and never started, by highway locomotives and electric cars. Of all these, the steam car was at first the best developed. The gasoline-velocipede or buggy was just one more variety. And, like the others, it generally retained the shape of one of the established horse-drawn vehicles, partly because it was the custom, partly because there was no other kind to be purchased. The early drivers and mechanics were too taken up with their motors to worry about streamlining.

Among these ingenious men, Gottlieb Daimler of Württemberg was probably the most important pioneer. He was employed for ten years at the machine works of Otto, and also spent much time in machine shops at home and abroad; the new industry was one that had to be learned at first hand. When he was fifty years old, he set up a shop of his own, and began to turn out automobiles; a few at a time, European fashion. They had cone-clutches, gears that gave more speeds than one, water jackets to cool the cylinder, suction jet carburetors, and cylinders set V-shape. He named one of his cars after his daughter—the Mercedes. At the same time another product of German machine shops, Carl Benz, using earlier experiments, constructed a gasoline tricycle with a leather belt to transmit the power from motor to wheel, instead of the chain employed by Daimler. This was the first of those midget cars that have always remained popular in Europe because of their low horse-power and small fuel consumption, and because of the high taxes on larger engines. It used the narrow rubber tires and the wire spokes of the bicycle wheel. The motor, like Daimler's, was located at the rear of the car, the horizontal flywheel occupying about the same general space that the differential does today.

In 1886 the Frenchman, Levassor, obtained in his country the rights to the German patents. Financed by a man named Panhard, he began to manufacture motor vehicles, gradually adding to them his own striking improvements. He set the motor in the front of the car, flywheel upright, and placed the radiator ahead of it, in order that the latter should get the full benefit of the cooling rush of the passing air. He raised the body from the chassis by means of elliptical springs, thus saving the motor from many hard jolts, and incidentally making the passengers more comfortable; in those days the builder had to think of the motor first, last, and always. The innovations of Levassor were sound, and were not discarded. With them, the automobile began to suggest the car of today. At least, it had all the essential structural features.

AMERICA TINKERS

Meanwhile, news of these revolutionary inventions had been trickling across the Atlantic Ocean, and setting numerous mechanics, inventors, and "cranks" to work. Men from bicycle shops and carriage factories, men who worked in steam and electric plants became interested. Many who had no more equipment than a few tools and a junk heap started tinkering with the problem of making a horseless carriage of their own, and perhaps improving it with a few Yankee gadgets. As early as 1879 George B. Seldon of Rochester had applied for patents on a vehicle driven by an internal combustion engine, although due to ill luck and financial difficulties he never got further than building the motor. In 1895 his patents were granted and came eventually to be controlled by an association called the Licensed Automobile Manufacturers. This association made a considerable amount of money, but was finally brought to an end when Henry Ford, after a ten years' suit, proved that, because his car used an engine of the Otto type, he was not infringing on the Seldon patents. Since practically all gasoline vehicles used Otto engines, the whole matter was

HENRY FORD
Whose engineering ability contributed to
making the automobile inexpensive and
practical.

thus settled, though not until the Licensed Automobile Manufacturers had collected as much as two million dollars in royalties.
During the hottest part of the fight, Ford's adversaries built a car
according to Seldon's specifications and drove it up and down in
New York City; Ford retaliated by doing the same with a French
car that antedated Seldon's first patent applications.

A Benz car was exhibited at the Chicago World's Fair in 1893.
It gave the American experimenters something to look at, something that had proved its worth. Doubtless the fingers of many
of them itched to take the thing apart and see just what made
it work; perhaps some of them did! At all events, gasoline automobiles began to chug about and stall in the crowded streets and
along the deep-rutted country roads, much to the excitement and
amusement of onlookers. Many a horse passed proudly by while
its driver smiled at the increasingly familiar sight of a pair of feet
sticking out from under a silent, motionless chassis.

Charles E. Duryea was the man who constructed the first gasoline vehicle successful in America. He and his brother Frank, able

Evolution of

1899   1902

COURTESY MOTOR

1916   1928

the Automobile

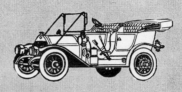

1904   1911

COURTESY MOTOR

1931   1934

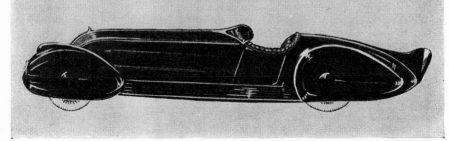

Courtesy Esquire

Courtesy Isotta Motors, N. Y.   Photo by General Photographic Service

COLLAPSIBLE CABRIOLET OF 1924-5

young mechanics, put together car after car; their fifth, a four-cylinder model equipped with pneumatic tires, finally satisfied them. By keeping this going at an average speed of ten miles an hour they won the first American automobile race, one from Chicago to Waukegan. Later they took two cars to England, where they astonished everyone by winning the fifty-two mile race from London to Brighton, finishing an hour ahead of some famous French models. This was just a short time after an English law had been repealed which limited the speed of horseless vehicles to four miles an hour, and required that they be preceded by a man carrying a red flag. It was a strange law but at that same time many people, alarmed at the growing number of accidents, were agitating for such a law in America.

Duryea might have become the leader of his industry, but he seemed to be somewhat stubborn about introducing any further improvements; for example, he retained the steering lever, today seen in only a few electrics, when others were adopting the steering wheel. He organized several companies but was never very successful. However, the position he might have taken was ably filled by several others, chief among them being Henry Ford.

MASS PRODUCTION

The qualities of Ford's personality were typical of the early American automobile makers, save that he possessed them to a greater degree than most of his contemporaries. All were men who, almost without exception, had come up through the ranks, who had come to understand motors by getting their fingers greasy. The Dodge brothers and John N. Willy were bicycle dealers, Elwood Haynes was a metallurgist; the Studebaker brothers were blacksmiths and woodworkers; others were machinists, toolmakers, and salesmen. For every one that succeeded, there were a hundred that failed. The industry was considered a fad; no big money was going into it; few well-known engineers were concerned with it. It had to push its way.

Like the others, Ford had an insatiable curiosity about all things mechanical. At the age of thirteen he took a watch apart, found out what made it work and, unlike most other boys, put it together again. Thereafter he repaired watches for neighbors, and dreamed of making them cheaply in large quantities. Three years later, against the wishes of his farmer father, he walked to Detroit and got a position in a machine shop, working with a jeweler in his spare time. Two years later he shifted to another

Courtesy Reo Motor Car Co.

THE REO 2-3 TON TRUCK

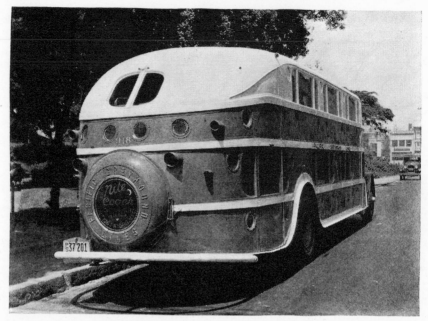

A MODERN NIGHT COACH (SLEEPER BUS)

machine shop, then got a job installing small steam engines. He was getting his knowledge at first hand, and he was always thinking of quantity production; for a time he was interested in designing a steam tractor for ploughing, small and cheap enough to be within reach of the purse of almost any farmer. But when he accepted a position with the Detroit Edison Company, and began making a gasoline car in his spare time, he came into his own.

Ford's first car was no stranger than many made at that time, but today it would present a queer sight. It had bicycle wheels with gas-pipe hubs, a buggy seat and a two-cylinder engine constructed from other oddments of old pipe. He took the first trip in it one rainy night. His wife ran alongside and held an umbrella over him. It worked! Even the second speed of twenty miles an hour worked! A few weeks later he sold it and began to build another.

That was in 1893. It took Ford ten years to organize a company that would not fall apart because of disagreements between

himself and the directors, ten years to convince even a few people
that a low-priced car, a car for the average man, was feasible. All
the while he was sifting the innovations that were being made in
America and Europe, discarding all parts that were not essential,
all parts that could not be easily made by machinery and in quantity. He introduced the practice of progressive assembling into his
plant; moving conveyors carried each car past different groups
of machinists, who built it up rapidly from rear axle and driving
shaft to finished product. The result was the famous Model T, a
car that was easy to drive and that almost anyone could repair, a
car without unnecessary parts or embellishments, a car that could
be painted any color the customer wanted, "so long as it was
black!"

In ways such as this the automobile came into general use, and
now each year sees new advances, new refinements. The motor is
almost silent. The self-starter, invented by Charles F. Kettering,
is now universally used. The interior is fitted out more luxuriously than many homes. Factors of safety have been greatly increased.
The natural beauty of the streamlined body is doing away with
the last few hints of the parent carriages and tricycles. Streamlining may make the car of the future look even more like a
tear-drop; the rear-end engine may possibly be revived. There is
no end to the improvements possible. Man may come to take the
automobile even more for granted than he does today.

But there are still some traces left of its rugged, helter-skelter
infancy. When Admiral Byrd successfully introduced the snow-
mobile to the Antarctic, the driver had still to get down and blow
out the feed tube.

THE TRACTOR AND CRAWLER TREAD

SLAVES AND OXEN pulled the primitive farm implements and carts used for centuries before the Industrial Revolution. Spirited horses dashed into battle pulling chariots and gun carriages. When the age of machinery gathered momentum in the nineteenth century, animals still furnished the power to move agricultural and military implements. Even now the horse and the mule are widely used in farming and warfare, but the crawler- and wheel-tractors have made great inroads in the work where once animals were supreme. Cugnot, in France, saw the need of a heavy machine for hauling artillery and as a result built his steam tractor which is often referred to as the forerunner of the automobile.

Some of the first attempts to apply steam power to farming were made by Fowler and Smith in England in 1854. Steam engines were stationed at the ends of fields to pull plows back and forth by cable attachments. This method of plowing was not adaptable to the large fields of America, and in 1888 Jacob Price built a steam engine that could pull several plows behind it. Benjamin Holt, at Stockton, California, designed a tremendous machine with wheels eighteen feet wide, but its use was not practicable because the wheels packed the soil too hard. In an attempt to obtain the traction necessary to pull farm machinery, Holt developed the lag-bed, already invented by Keeley in England early in the nineteenth century.

The lag-bed is a continuous belt track which is laid down and picked up by sprocket wheels. W. P. Miller in California made a hinged lag-bed for steam engines; but Alvin Lombard, in Maine, obtained a patent in 1901 for the first practical tractor of this type. Holt made an improved type of lag-bed for his tractor in 1903, which was first powered by steam and then by the newly-developed internal combustion engine. The track of a modern crawler tractor is built in hinged sections with lugs to prevent slipping. A chain attachment is fixed on the inside of the track,

Courtesy Allis-Chalmers Co.

MODERN COMBINE AT WORK ON AN INDIANA FARM

turned by a sprocket wheel at either end. Rollers at the top of the unit hold the track from sagging, and at the bottom the chain passes under a skid or runner. This tractor practically "picks itself up by its boot straps," and large ones used on farms can do the work of twenty horses.

WINTER LOGGING OPERATIONS WITH TRACK-TYPE TRACTORS
ON THE WEST COAST

THE TANK—A FIGHTING TRACTOR

Used widely in agricultural and road-building operations, the tractor has had important applications in warfare.

The lag-bed principle makes it possible for a heavy machine to move easily over loose, rough, or boggy soil without miring. Obstructions, such as ditch banks, mounds, and narrow trenches, offer only slight hindrance to the progress of this crawling tractor. During the World War, large and small tanks were built with long tractor treads. They were formidable offensive weapons, mounting machine guns which could be operated with comparative safety by soldiers protected from enemy fire. Moving ponderously over trenches and barbed-wire entanglements, the tanks spread terror as they rolled across the battlefields. Military engineers have developed small tanks which can be maneuvered easily and quickly whether in "mopping-up" tactics against captured cities, or on the varied terrain of the field of combat.

PEACEFUL PROGRESS

It was the internal combustion engine that made possible the large-scale production of tractors needed for agricultural production. There was a labor shortage on American farms even before the World War. The introduction of such machines as efficient plows, grain drills, reapers and harvesters, and tillage implements partly solved the problem. But to pull this heavy machinery, horses were expensive and steam engines were far from satisfactory. In 1896 two Iowa inventors, C. H. Parr and C. W. Hart, built a factory in Madison, Wisconsin, to manufacture the oil-cooled engine. Their first tractor had only one cylinder, but it was so successful that fifteen years of use did not entirely wear it out. Hart and Parr moved to Charles City, Iowa, in 1901, and in the next year they built fifteen tractors. Two years later they had an engine that would burn kerosene, a fuel more plentiful and cheaper at that time than gasoline.

Many manufacturers entered the field after the success of the tractor was demonstrated. Hart-Parr, Avery, Rumley, and Mogul were some of the names familiar in the tractor field. Truly mass production came into vogue with the Fordson, the McCormick-Deering, and others. Diesel engines were used, as well as the internal combustion type. Wheel tractors, produced at moderate cost by the thousand, came into use all over the world. Later huge rubber tires were used instead of steel wheels for certain types of farm work.

Former unwieldy machines have been reduced in size, and there is hardly an agricultural operation in which tractors cannot be employed. They pull plows, harrows, discs, harvesters, and wagons. They furnish power for threshing, baling hay, filling silos, shelling corn, sawing wood, grinding feed, and other tasks. Various fuels, from gasoline to unrefined oil, are used. And when the day's work is done, the farmer merely shuts off the ignition. Large farms can be operated without any horses at all.

AFTER VAINLY FLAPPING HIS WINGS

FROM EARLIEST TIMES men's minds have been fascinated by the idea of soaring above the surface of the earth. To the primitive mentality the only technique which suggested itself was that used by birds. The mythical ascent of Daedalus and Icarus presaged many attempts at flight by muscular effort. But after centuries of vainly flapping his wings man discovered the density of air and with it the possibility of mounting through it like a bubble through water. This was the basis of the search for lighter-than-air methods by means of which the great modern airships such as the *Graf Zeppelin* can soar through space.

Before the age of scientific experiment many thinkers speculated on the possibility of flight. As early as the thirteenth century Roger Bacon pondered the notion. But the imaginings of many of these early strivers were unbelievably fantastic. Joseph Galien, a French friar, held that he could construct a cube-shaped balloon which would lift more than seven and a half billion pounds, and his vague scheme was no more absurd than many others of the time.

ALOFT WITH A CANDY EGG

The first actual experiments with balloons were made in Paris by Joseph and Etienne Montgolfier. Filling paper-lined bags with smoke, they demonstrated in 1783 the results of their work of the previous year, and their balloon rose more than a mile in the air and traveled a mile and a half before descending. In the same year the Académie des Sciences commissioned Professor J. A. C. Charles and the Robert brothers to make a balloon, and these men filled their rubber-varnished bag with hydrogen gas—the first time this gas was so used—and it traveled fifteen miles, caus-

Paul's Photos, Chicago

EARLY BALLOONS WERE GAUDY AFFAIRS, HIGHLY DECORATED

ing much amazement among the people of the countryside where it fell. Neither of these balloons carried any weight other than that of their own composition, but the Montgolfiers, in a demonstration before Louis XVI two weeks later, sent up another garishly ornamented *globe aerostatique,* this time carrying a duck, a rooster, and a sheep.

Still under the delusion that the warm air which made their balloons rise was some sort of gas generated by the flames, the Montgolfiers soon began to look about for a human being to be sent aloft in their "globe." They found their man in the person of daring Jean François Pilâtre de Rozier, who insisted on going up in place of the condemned criminals whose employment had been suggested. In another of the brothers' gaudy balloons, which more than anything else resembled children's Easter eggs, De Rozier made his heroic ascent, the first in the history of mankind. The balloon, anchored by ropes to the earth, rose to a height of eighty-four feet, and here De Rozier stayed for several minutes, feeding the grate fire in his wicker basket. A little more than a month later De Rozier and a friend made the first flight in a free balloon, successfully sailing about over Paris.

TWO SUNSETS IN THE SAME DAY

Early in December, 1783, Professor Charles, with one of the Robert brothers, mounted into the air in another hydrogen balloon and traveled twenty-seven miles. At the end of this distance the balloon settled and Charles' passenger alighted. Its load lightened, the balloon again took to the air just after sunset, and again Charles saw the sun as he rose. For the second time that day he watched it descend and set. This was the golden age of ballooning; no fatal accidents had as yet occurred, and pioneering flights were made in many parts of the world. Perhaps the outstanding one among these early fliers was Jean Pierre Blanchard, who accomplished the first aerial crossing of the English Channel, as well as more than sixty epic flights in most of the countries of Europe and in America.

But the year 1785 saw the death of De Rozier, first to ascend and first to die in a crash. His fatal flight was made in a twofold aerostat, one part of which was lifted by hydrogen gas and the other by a fire and warmed air. The inevitable happened. A spark from the fire of one part flew into the hydrogen container of the other, and the gas exploded, killing De Rozier and his backer, Romaine.

FROZEN, SOAKED, AND FROZEN AGAIN

The world was aghast at this tragic event, and the art of flying experienced a definite setback; it was not until the early years of the nineteenth century that ascents again began to be made in large numbers. Cittadino Zambeccari was among the first, although not among the most fortunate, who figured in the revival. According to his rather exaggerated account, he, with two companions, rose prematurely one night in 1803 to a height of five miles, where they suffered intensely from the frigid air. They then dropped suddenly into the Adriatic Sea, but ascended again so high that the water in which they had been immersed froze on them and they were again tortured by the cold of the upper

Paul's Photos, Chicago

THE GRAF ZEPPELIN ON ITS FIRST FLIGHT TO AMERICA

air. They then descended again into the sea and floated about for more than a day before they were rescued.

Among the other fliers of this period were Gay-Lussac and Biot, who made several flights carrying scientific measuring devices in 1803, and the years following; Wise, who in 1816 flew from St. Louis to Henderson, New York; Arban, who made the first crossing of the Alps by air; and Charles Green, who flew in 1836 from England to Germany, a distance of five hundred miles, in eighteen hours.

It was Green who devised the guide rope as a partial substitute for ballast; when a balloon sank so low that the rope trailed on the ground, the lifting capacity was automatically relieved of some weight; the lower the balloon sank, the less rope it had to carry, and, with reduced weight, it would tend to rise again. The cylindrical shape was by this time well established among balloon makers. The ballonet, first suggested in 1783 by General Meusnier, had been in use since 1816; this was a small bag within the balloon, which was inflated or deflated by a bellows to keep the shape of the balloon as the air pressure varied with ascent or descent. The ideas of Sir George Cayley, the "father of British aeronautics," were coming into use—the principles of streamlining and the idea of a subdivided hull which when punctured would not allow complete leakage of gas.

THE MAIL THAT WENT ASTRAY

In the Civil War the practicality of observation balloons was made evident, through the efforts of Professor Thaddeus Lowe. Their use in the taking of aerial photographs had already been pioneered by Felix Nadar, whose real name was Felix Tournachon, in 1858. Tournachon also organized the *Ballon Poste,* which carried mail from Paris when it was besieged in the Franco-Prussian War. These balloons succeeded in taking almost twelve tons of mail out of the isolated city, although they often went astray, two traveling as far as Norway before they descended.

It became clear in the earliest days of ballooning that a solution of the problems of directional control was necessary. The

BUILDING A GIANT DIRIGIBLE

Picture shows fins being put in place on the U. S. S. Akron.

free balloon could sail only as the wind blew, and it was lucky that Europe was in the path of the prevailing westerly winds, which prevented many of the balloonists who were wafted about the Continent from drifting out over the Atlantic. Such weird methods as gigantic oars, revolving gas bags, waving fins, and undulating chains of balloons were suggested, and some of them were tried. In 1843 Monck Mason achieved a small degree of success in bucking the wind with an Archimedean screw driven by clockwork.

Steam power was attempted in flight control by Henri Giffard in 1852, but the proportion of weight of his power plant to that of the total lifting capacity of the balloon was an almost insurmountable obstacle, and in addition he was in constant fear that a spark from his boiler fire might ignite the hydrogen in the gas bag. In spite of this, however, he was able to make perceptible progress against the wind. In the same year the use of rocket power was suggested by James Nye, but until very recently nothing was actually done with this technique. Twenty years later Paul Haenlein, in a semi-rigid dirigible, made the first successful flight powered by a coal gas engine; and, ten years after this, Albert and Gaston Tissandier achieved slight successes with an electric motor run by wet-cell batteries.

In 1884, two years after the Tissandiers had first applied the method, Charles Renard and A. C. Kreb designed a balloon propelled by a battery-driven motor. This was a definitely effective airship; it made six flights and in all of them was able to return to its starting point. The first use of a gasoline engine to propel a balloon was made in 1897, and it was made in the first rigid balloon. Designed by Schwarz, the airship was constructed of aluminum eight thousandths of an inch in thickness, with aluminum tubular reinforcement. Also embodying the principle of separated gas chambers, this design was far in advance of its time. Its flight was not successful, however, and it settled ignominiously to earth when a considerable amount of gas leaked out.

A PLAYBOY WITH A KITE

One of the most famous of all the fliers in Paris at the turn of the century was Alberto Santos-Dumont, the adventurous son of a rich Brazilian. He rapidly passed through the whole evolution of lighter-than-air flight, beginning with a free balloon. One of his early flights would have ended disastrously had he not been able, by shouting, to attract the attention of some boys in a field, whom he directed to pull his craft into the wind as they would a kite. He made several flights using illuminating gas instead of hydrogen gas for his lifting power. His later flights were very successful, and in 1901 he won the Deutsch prize of a hundred thousand francs for circumnavigating the Eiffel Tower, starting from and returning to the suburb of St. Cloud. It was not long after the flights of Santos-Dumont that the Lebaudy brothers and others began to build airships for the use of governments. France, Russia, England, and other countries purchased airships, which, though not always successful, made possible the work of Zeppelin.

In 1900 Count Ferdinand von Zeppelin completed, after two years of painstaking work, his first rigid airship. It attained a speed of nearly eighteen miles an hour in its second flight, and

Courtesy Goodyear Tire & Rubber Co.

APPLYING OUTER COVERING TO STERN OF A LIGHTER-THAN-AIR CRAFT

Paul's Photos, Chicago

RETURN OF THE GRAF ZEPPELIN
The famous ship is shown landing at Friedrichshafen, Germany, after completing its
first transatlantic voyage.

tolled the knell of attempts to do practical flying in non-rigid or semi-rigid ships. Zeppelin continued the construction of successful models, and with the beginning of his third received government aid. As early as 1910 the count's airships were engaged in regularly scheduled passenger service. German construction of airships was tremendously accelerated by the outbreak of the World War in 1914. The great ships were not as effective as instruments of war as the Germans had hoped, but they took a very definite toll, as much in the effect on British morale and the necessity of maintaining overmanned defenses in England as in the actual destruction wrought by their bombs.

THE FATE OF THE MAMMOTH?

Recent history of the airship has not been very encouraging. The nations of the world set about building larger and speedier craft, which performed brilliantly for a time but in almost every case met with disaster. The English "R-34" crossed the Atlantic in 1919, the first lighter-than-air transoceanic flight, but it was later wrecked. In 1926 Roald Amundsen crossed the North Pole in the *Norge,* now withdrawn from service, but General Umberto Nobile, one of Amundsen's companions, was lost when the *Italia* crashed in its return after the same achievement. Attempts at rescue saved Nobile and some of his crew, but cost the lives of rescuers, including that of Amundsen himself. British airship history has seen the disaster of the "R-38," the explosion of the great "R-101," and the scrapping of the "R-100." The *Roma,* Italian-built semi-rigid, crashed on a high tension power line in Virginia in 1922. The German "L-72," acquired by France after the Treaty of Versailles and renamed the *Dixmude,* was lost somewhere in the Mediterranean in 1923.

In the United States the *Shenandoah* tragedy in 1925 presaged the disasters of the mighty naval ships, the *Akron* and the *Macon* in 1933 and 1935. The *Los Angeles,* German-constructed, is inactive. The reputation of the Germans themselves for successes in lighter-than-air travel was rudely shattered when in the spring of 1937 the gigantic *Hindenburg* crashed at Lakehurst after completion of several scheduled transatlantic flights. The ship, inflated with hydrogen, crashed in flames as she was about to land after another crossing. The *Graf Zeppelin,* virtually the last of the titans in active service, seems to bear a charmed existence. Completed in 1928, the giant airship, with its renowned commander, Dr. Hugo Eckener, was the first lighter-than-air craft to circumnavigate the earth, which it did in 1929 in the record-breaking time of twenty-one days, seven hours, and

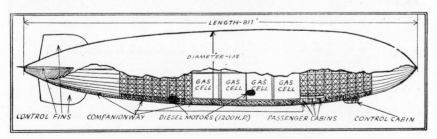

SECTIONAL PLAN OF THE *HINDENBURG*

International News photo

THE TRAGIC END OF THE GREAT DIRIGIBLE *HINDENBURG*,
MAY 6, 1937

thirty-four minutes. In this flight it set a non-stop distance mark of 6,980 miles, from Germany to Japan. The future of these mammoths of the air is subject to conjecture. Whether they will suffer the fate of the prehistoric beasts and be abandoned as a costly waste of life; or whether they will again rise, with safe helium replacing unsafe hydrogen, overcoming the difficulties that have made them "white elephants" in the past, remains in doubt. The continued success of the *Graf Zeppelin* encourages belief that lighter-than-air flight is feasible.

LACEWORK OF GIRDERS

The *Graf Zeppelin*, typical of the great airships as well as their most conspicuous example of success, is constructed of an intricate network of girders. Within these are the gas compartments, and over all is a tightly stretched coating of several layers of specially treated fabric. The "Graf" is 776 feet in length and has a diameter of one hundred feet. The pilot house is built into the hull, and the five engines are slung beneath—two amidships on either side, and one well toward the stern. In the *Macon* and *Akron* the engines were housed within the hull, only the propellers projecting. There are four fins: two are vertical rudders rising above and below the streamlined stern; and two are horizontal elevators. The Maybach engines are driven by Blau gas, an extremely light fuel of approximately the same heaviness as air. The disaster of the *Hindenburg* made it clear that if lighter-than-air travel is ever to attain real safety, hydrogen gas must be abandoned as a lifting agency in favor of the non-inflammable helium. The use of this gas has been limited in the past because it is obtainable in practical quantities only in the United States. Although its lifting capacity is appreciably less than that of hydrogen, it is apparently the only feasible means to airship operation in the long run.

The essential difficulty in lighter-than-air flight, however, is the principle of airship flying itself. Necessarily built light for flying, the airship is subject to the violent buffeting of winds and storms. Its flight, in contrast to that of heavier-than-air craft, is comparable to that of a monstrous canoe built to cross an ocean. Until some method is devised to meet this obstacle, perhaps by ascension into the higher atmosphere above the zone of weather disturbances, airship travel will be in grave danger of extinction.

TWENTY-FOUR CENTURIES OF GROWTH

ALTHOUGH THE AIRPLANE is ranked as the scientific wonder-child of the twentieth century, dramatically brought into being with the flight of the Wright brothers in the windy fields of Kitty Hawk in 1903, its history actually ranges over twenty-four centuries. Its birth is wrapped in legend.

The ancient Chinese are said to have developed small helicopters made with feathers, but if they did the achievement was buried in the obscurity of oriental history long before Western civilization was born. The progenitor of modern flying was the wooden dove, said to have been constructed by Archytas, a Greek geometer, in 400 B.C. There is no record of the mechanism of Archytas' bird, and that it really could have flown seems incredible in that age of primitive mechanics. The next scene of reported aviation is the Rome of Nero's day, where early mechanics are said to have experimented with rudimentary gliders, most of which ended in disaster.

Authentic history of heavier-than-air flying begins with the inventions and drawings of that most versatile of all geniuses, Leonardo da Vinci, in the sixteenth century. By some quirk of accident, da Vinci's best-known accomplishments in aeronautics are his drawings of helicopters and ornithopters, early ancestors of the airplane. In reality, his most important contribution was his description of the aerial screw from which has stemmed all present-day successful flying and all high-speed marine transportation—for the marine propeller is a derivative of the aerial screw and not vice versa, as is generally supposed.

Throughout the sixteenth and seventeenth centuries a long line of intrepid experimenters attempted flight with elementary gliders and paddle-shaped wings. In 1809 Sir George Cayley anticipated the modern scientific basis of flight with his invention of a rigid

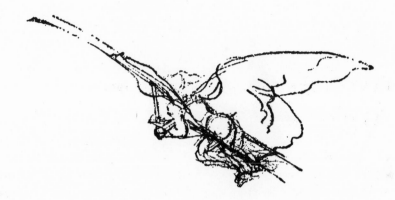

ONE OF DA VINCI'S BIRDMEN SKETCHES

mechanism driven through the air by propellers connected to an efficient source of mechanical power. He proposed using the internal combustion engine, which was later to prove itself efficient, but in those early days was a curiosity that worked spasmodically. Cayley soon deserted heavier-than-air navigation for lighter-than-air ascension, and the practical pioneering with his discovery was carried on by William Samuel Henson and John Stringfellow, who in 1844 constructed the world's first powered airplane capable of continuous and directed flight. In 1867 Stringfellow made a second craft, a triplane, which was placed on exhibit at the First Aeronautical Exhibition in London. The world came to gape. The plane failed to fly when tried; but scientifically, if not practically, heavier-than-air transport had been born.

Between Stringfellow's invention and the Wright brothers' flight, aviation was pushed forward by other adventurous scientists. In 1879 Victor Tatin built a twin-screw monoplane mounted on wheels, driven by a compressed-air engine. In 1875 Thomas Moy introduced his newly devised steam engine into air travel. Neither of these solved the problem of powering an airplane.

Another major handicap of all planes in the Henson and Stringfellow era had been clumsy wing construction. It was not until 1903 that the Wright brothers brought forth the first scientifically designed wing—a curved shape effectively using the con-

Paul's Photos, Chicago

KRONFIELD, AUSTRIAN CHAMPION, PUTTING HIS GLIDER
THROUGH ITS PACES

cave lower surface and the convex upper surface. In powering and mechanism the airplane was on the verge of spectacular developments at the dawn of the twentieth century.

THE MIRACLE AT KITTY HAWK

Profiting by the painful experimentation of European scientists, three Americans made aviation a practical means of transport just as flying was entering the twenty-fourth century of its history. Samuel Pierpont Langley, mathematician, astronomer, and physicist, broadened the scientific basis of heavier-than-air travel with his studies of aerodynamics. He built several planes but they never flew. Most famous was his *Aerodrome,* a kite-like airplane launched from a boat, with which he experimented near Washington, D. C. Its first flight ended in disaster; it unceremoniously moved along its launching device and fell into the river. Newspapermen of that day reported that aviation was still an unsuccessful experiment. Langley never flew his craft, but in 1908 some men resurrected his *Aerodrome,* repaired it and modified it, and it flew. But in 1908 men had already learned to fly under the tutelage of the Wright brothers.

Simultaneously with Langley, Wilbur and Orville Wright of Dayton, Ohio, had been experimenting tirelessly with glider and airplane construction. In December, 1903, they took their most successful airplane to Kitty Hawk, North Carolina, and there, piloted by Wilbur, it covered a distance of eight hundred and fifty-two feet and remained in the air fifty-nine seconds. On landing it crashed and was so severely damaged that it was never flown again, but the Wrights built a new plane and resumed their experiments in a Dayton cow pasture. In three years of experiment, they increased their distance from eight hundred and fifty-two feet to twenty-four miles and their speed from thirty to thirty-eight miles per hour and contributed the "joystick" to aviation mechanism. The era of heavier-than-air travel was successfully launched.

Courtesy Museum of Science and Industry, Chicago

WRIGHT BROTHERS AIRPLANE, MODEL B, BUILT IN 1911-12

United Air Lines photo

RADIAL ENGINE OF A MODERN AIR TRANSPORT

FRONT VIEW OF THE ITALIAN SEAPLANE *SAVOIA MARCHETTI*

TESTING IN THE SKY

From that time on, the history of aviation was a series of epochal flights. The most rapid progress was made in France and in the United States. In 1908 Wilbur Wright established the world's first endurance record of two hours eighteen minutes and thirty-three seconds over the fields of France, for Frenchmen had proved to be more interested in his experiments than had his American neighbors. In 1909 Louis Bleriot, a pioneer aviator of France, made the first heavier-than-air flight across the English Channel. In the same year Orville Wright designed the first military airplane, winning a prize of $25,000 offered by the United States War Department.

AIRCRAFT DURING THE WAR AND AFTER

The World War precipitated aviation from callow adolescence into full maturity. Despite the fact that the Hague Peace Conference had solemnly gone on record against their use to discharge projectiles and explosives, airplanes soon became one of the chief instruments of destruction. With the inventions of Anthony

H. G. Fokker, a "flying" Dutchman who offered his services to Germany when they had been refused by the Allies as too expensive, the plane became an active, mobile fighting unit. Under the pressure of war needs enormous strides were made in construction. The multi-motored type of plane was evolved. Seaplanes, formerly crude and unreliable, suddenly became extremely efficient means of transport.

When the war was over, a large and enthusiastic group of aviators turned their attention to the problems of spanning the Atlantic. This was a project that had stimulated the public imagination before 1914 to the point where London newspapers had offered prizes for its achievement in a flight of less than seventy-two hours. The first heavier-than-air craft to cross the Atlantic was the United States navy plane NC-4, which in 1919 flew from Newfoundland to Plymouth, England, in three stages. A few months later Captain John Alcock and Lieutenant Arthur Whitten Brown achieved the first non-stop flight from Newfoundland to Ireland and won a prize offered by the *London Daily Mail*.

LINDBERGH—GALAHAD OF THE AIR

It was the New York-Paris flight of Charles A. Lindbergh eight years later, however, which launched the era of transatlantic flying. Because he was young, because he flew alone, because he was unostentatious, Colonel Lindbergh aroused world enthusiasm not only for his exploit but for aviation as a means of transport. The golden day of heavier-than-air travel was ushered in.

From that time on the world began to be girdled by airlines. The Pacific was spanned in successive flights from California to Hawaii, California to Australia and California to China. Pioneering aviators linked Australia and Africa, London and Australia, Cairo and Capetown, San Francisco and New York, by air. The first round-the-world flight was made by United States army planes in 1924, but it was the spectacular flight of Harold Gatty and Wiley Post in 1931 that placed globe-girdling by air in the public imagination.

Today the powerful planes of Pan-American Airways, British Imperial Airways, Air France, and half a dozen smaller lines

Paul's Photos, Chicago

THE GLOSTER BOMBER-TRANSPORT (GREAT BRITAIN)
It can carry thirty men with full equipment.

Herbert Photos, N. Y.

GIANT GERMAN PLANE, THE DORNIER *DO-X*
Compare with the ordinary biplane in upper left of picture.

Courtesy American Airlines, Inc.

AN AMERICAN SLEEPER PLANE HIGH OVER THE DESERT

Photo by American Airlines, Inc.

SLEEPING BERTHS ON AN AIRLINER OF 1937

Paul's Photos, Chicago
THE WILFORD GYROPLANE IN DEMONSTRATION FLIGHT

Paul's Photos, Chicago   AN AIRPORT BROADCASTING STATION
Operators receive weather reports and other information over the teletype, which is then
broadcast to pilots in flight.

Courtesy United Airlines

A NEW DOUGLAS AIRLINER IN FLIGHT

carry on regular commercial air service between the United States
and China, North and South America, England and South Africa,
Europe and South America, western Europe and eastern Asia.
Only two major air routes remain to be established: one from New
York to London via the North Atlantic, and one from New York
to Continental Europe via Bermuda and the Azores. The former
seems likely soon to be realized in the projected service, already the

subject of test flights, of Pan-American Airways and Imperial Airways between Harbor Grace, Newfoundland, and Foynes, Ireland.

Today sleek planes course through the skies bearing thousands of passengers daily. Departures of airplanes from airports are scheduled in the same manner as are railway trains. Planes leave the airport with a regularity and efficiency that contrasts sharply with the "waiting for the wind" that characterized flying in the early days.

The airliners themselves are marvels of efficiency and beauty. Streamlining to bring about the utmost flying efficiency has also made airplanes objects of beauty. Well insulated cabins and provisions for the comfort of passengers have made air travel comfortable as well as thrilling. Duplicate controls, blind flying, twin motors, and alternate pilots increase the safety of flying. On the overseas flights of commerical air lines a number of special officers make possible efficient flying. An engineer checks the operation of the motors, a navigator determines the course to be flown, and a radioman keeps the plane in constant communication with weather stations and ground crews.

MAN BUILDS, THEN
DESTROYS
Anti-aircraft guns designed to bring proud queens of the air to earth in flaming ruins. Note the camouflage of branches causing this gun to look like a tree trunk.

VISITS TO OUR PLANETARY NEIGHBORS

SENSITIVE PERSONS, looking up into the clear night sky, often feel the presence of a great mystery. What, they wonder, is up there? What are the planets like? How can we reach them? Beyond the confines of earth, in outer space, thrilling adventures await us. Imaginative minds are even now planning man's greatest adventure—interplanetary travel. This, however, is acknowledged by even the most enthusiastic to be only a fanciful dream at present. The sole remote hope of accomplishing it seems to lie in the rocket ship.

But the rocket is not being developed merely with an eye toward travel to the moon and planets. More immediate engineering applications are sought. Men of scientific ability and imagination have, during the last three or four decades, been speculating on the uses of the rocket principle in our daily affairs. A number of improvements have been made during the past twenty-five years which have increased both the efficiency and the effectiveness of the device. Until these recent developments, few fundamental improvements were made in rockets over those used in ancient times.

Robert Esnault-Pelterie, a French engineer who had much to do with early airplane development, completed calculations in 1907 to show the possibility of high-speed rocket transportation. But to Dr. Robert H. Goddard, professor at Clark University, Worcester, Massachusetts, belongs the honor of having done the first practical experiments in the field. His investigations began in 1909 and are still being carried on. In 1914 he developed the liquid-fuel rocket, which is much safer than the earlier explosive-powder types. Professor Goddard startled the scientific world in 1919 by publishing data showing that a flight to the moon was possible. His plan was to load a rocket with magnesium powder,

Paul's Photos, Chicago

REAR VIEW OF THE OPEL ROCKET CAR SHOWING CYLINDERS
FROM WHICH ROCKETS WERE DISCHARGED

which would explode on hitting the moon and give a great flash,
bright enough to be seen through earthly telescopes. Dr. Goddard
is now attempting to perfect rockets for exploring the extremely
high altitudes. In 1931 Goddard set up a laboratory in the Arizona desert for developing meteorological rockets, and has discovered several important principles. He has increased control
over the direction of flight and experimented with different kinds
of liquid fuels. His relatively small rockets have attained a speed
of 5,500 miles per hour. Conservatively, it may be said that there
is no reason why a well-equipped rocket should not penetrate far
beyond the highest altitudes hitherto attained, and return with
intact records of its travels. In geographical work and in warfare,
photographs taken from very high altitudes may be extremely
useful. A grant of $100,000 has been made by the Daniel and
Florence Guggenheim Foundation for these valuable experiments.
Dr. Goddard's advisers include such well-known men as Col.
Charles A. Lindbergh and Dr. R. A. Millikan.

International News photo

FRITZ VON OPEL IN HIS ROCKET PLANE

PROPELLING MEN AND MAIL

So far, no actual rocket vehicles of practical value have been made, although rockets have been attached to gliders, automobiles, and sleds, and a high rate of speed has been attained by some of these vehicles. Germany has contributed much to rocket development. Two German physicists, Max Valier (killed by a rocket in 1930) and Albert Mueller, did much mathematical work in rocketry. Their data were used by Fritz von Opel, an automobile manufacturer, who built and operated a rocket automobile in 1928. Opel's car, equipped with powder rockets, was driven at a speed of 124 miles per hour, but the fuel was exhausted in a few seconds.

The reason for this unsatisfactory performance lies in the fact that rockets applied to low-speed vehicles are very ineffective, the net efficiency being approximately three per cent. The efficiency increases as the speed increases, but even at the present world's record for airplanes and automobiles the efficiency would still be too low to be practicable. Rocket propulsion applied to such vehicles could be satisfactory only if the energy of the jet of gases were used in some special way, as with turbines, or large air nozzles known as "thrust augmenters."

The present widespread interest in rockets and rocket propulsion is due not so much to what has been accomplished as to the theoretical possibilities of the method. A tapered nozzle, which utilizes the expansive power of the gases, previously wasted, has increased the efficiency of the jet to a marked degree. Reinhold Tiling of Berlin, using black-powder rockets, has reached heights said to be as great as 26,000 feet. Similar powder rockets have been used to transmit mail over short distances. Soviet Russian experimenters, under government subsidy, are attempting to perfect rocket systems for sending mail and passengers over their immense country.

5,000 MILES AN HOUR!

Thus, one field of usefulness for rocket ships is high-altitude transportation over the earth. At a height of thirty miles, where the air is very thin, tremendous speeds may be attained—5,000 miles per hour is not impossible. The rocket is propelled by literally kicking itself through space—each explosion of its fuel causes a recoil which pushes the rocket forward. At this speed the journey from Berlin to New York would take forty-five minutes. A rocket flight from Chicago to New York would take twenty minutes. Sometime there may be a regular commercial service by rocket between the continents, although undoubtedly not for many years. Service probably will not be established for distances less than a thousand miles.

When men have developed practical rocket ships for earth transportation, they will look questioningly toward the far-off planets. Perhaps the aspect of rocket propulsion that has had the greatest popular appeal has been the theoretical possibility of reaching great heights in the atmosphere, far above the ceiling for balloons, and of even leaving the earth entirely. The improvement which may make such performances possible is the principle of the multiple rocket, or the step rocket. Such a rocket consists not of one, but of a series of successively smaller rockets, the lowest of the series being discarded when it has become empty of fuel, this continuing until the last rocket is fired. In this way, the weight of the empty rocket is at all times small in proportion to the weight of the fuel.

International News photo

OPEL'S ROCKET CAR SPEEDING 235 MILES PER HOUR

Rockets provided with nozzles and powered with liquid fuel may eventually be applied to high-speed, high-altitude planes, for theory indicates that rocket propulsion should be more efficient than ordinary engine and propeller propulsion for speeds over 600 miles per hour, and the thrust should be even greater in air of low density, such as the air in the stratosphere, than at sea-level.

Further, the use of liquid fuels, such as gasoline and liquid oxygen, has not only been an improvement in providing a fuel which has several times the energy of black powder, but has also made possible the use of a small combustion chamber, the liquids being forced in from tanks. In the case of powder rockets the chamber must be large enough to contain the entire charge. In spite of these advantages, however, technical difficulties have prevented a very rapid development of liquid-fuel rockets, and the heights so far reached are by no means as great as those which eventually will be attained.

TRIPS TO THE MOON?

Travel to the moon and planets, in the opinion of H. N. Russell, research director of Mt. Wilson Observatory, may be possible, but certainly not for many long decades. There are many obstacles in the way even when good ships are developed. Navigation must be very precise—much more so than it is now. The shock of taking off and landing must be overcome. Enough supplies will have to be carried to permit returning. Enough power must be available to overcome the gravitational pull of the earth and the planets, for no rocketeer likes to contemplate the vision of his ship whirling forever as a satellite of the moon because it lacks the power to leave its gravitational pull! Moreover, the greater the height that is reached, the more serious is the deviation of the rocket from the desired path. Automatic stabilization in flight may be obtained by the use of gyroscopes, but few investigators have made any attempt to secure such stabilization. The moon and planets will not support life; explorers will have to carry their own oxygen, and wear heavy metal suits. Many such difficulties must be worked out by the would-be celestial adventurers.

There is a growing interest in space rockets, or astronautics (literally "navigation to the stars"), and astronautic societies have been organized in the United States (now called the American Rocket Society), in Germany, and in England. Since 1927 the Rep-Hirsch prize for astronautics has been given in France from time to time to the person who, having made formal application for the prize, has, in the opinion of a committee of award, made the best contribution to the new science of astronautics. In the whole world, rocket societies total about three thousand members; the American Rocket Society has about three or four hundred members, and membership is steadily growing.

Rocketry today seems to be in the same position as aviation before the Wright brothers' experiments at Kitty Hawk. Technical development is advancing, however, and many famous scientists feel that the rocket is due for a sudden advance just as the airplane was forty years ago.

MYSTERY OF RUDOLF DIESEL

TRAGEDY AND MYSTERY gave unusual importance to the regular trip of the mail steamer from Antwerp to London on the night of September 29, 1913. Among the passengers was an inconspicuous German engineer, Dr. Rudolf Diesel. No one knows exactly what happened, but Diesel disappeared. Perhaps he fell overboard while standing at the rail. Foul play may have had a part in the tragic occurrence, but the mystery has never been solved. Thus came to a close the life of this practical scientist.

Rudolf Diesel was born in Paris in 1858, the son of German parents. He received a technical education and managed various engineering projects in the city of his birth. He was only eighteen years of age when Dr. N. A. Otto of Cologne perfected the internal combustion engine.

Diesel's interest was attracted to the new invention which was to have such a profound influence on industry and transportation. An internal combustion engine, using gasoline or similar fuel, was expensive to operate and the fire hazard was far from negligible. A carburetor was necessary to make a combustible mixture. Electric sparks ignited the fuel, and the expansive power of the gas forced down the piston which was connected to a drive shaft. Power to turn generators or drive shafts could be developed much more cheaply if oil rather than gasoline or kerosene could be used. This was the problem to which Diesel directed his inventive genius. He would design an internal combustion engine which did not require an electric ignition system, and which would use a mixture of oil and air rather than gasoline and air. His experiments proceeded during several years, and in 1892 he was ready to apply for patents. Three years later the first Diesel was constructed, and in 1898 Diesels were a feature of the Munich Exposition.

RUDOLF DIESEL
The inventor of the Diesel engine.

Paul's Photos

THE ENGINE WITHOUT SPARK PLUGS

This new type of engine departed radically from the principles developed by Otto, mainly in the type of fuel and the ignition. Akroyd Stuart devised a fuel spray in a heated bulb attachment at the top of the compression chamber even before Diesel's successful experiments improved the process. The first Diesels were four-cycle engines. An intake stroke by the piston draws air into the compression chamber. On the next, the second, stroke, the air is compressed until it exerts a pressure of five to six hundred pounds per square inch. This compressed air is very hot—about 1000° F.—and sufficient to ignite the fuel oil which is sprayed through nozzles into the compression chamber. The atomized oil is admitted at the top of the second, or compression, stroke, and continues for a short time during the third cycle. At this time the fuel burns with great rapidity, and the expanding gases from the combustion force the piston downward, delivering power to the

A DIESEL POWER
UNIT

Courtesy Hercules Motors
Corporation

shaft by means of a connecting rod. The momentum of this stroke carries the piston back up the cylinder to force the exhaust gases through a valve that opens for that purpose.

Later types of Diesel use a two-stroke cycle principle. The air is compressed on an up-stroke, the fuel is sprayed into the chamber and its ignition causes the power-stroke. Near the end of this second stroke the exhaust gases are discharged through a scavenging valve, and an instant later pure air under pressure is forced into the cylinder. The valves close and the fresh air supply is once more compressed on the return stroke, continuing the process. The two-stroke cycle has about the same efficiency as the four-stroke, but a Diesel using this design is lighter and simpler, and may readily be operated in a reverse direction.

Each of these types of Diesel has a serious disadvantage in that the power impulse is applied only once in the cycle. In the four-stroke cycle, only one in four strokes of the piston carries power to the crankshaft; in the two-stroke cycle, the impulse is given on alternate strokes. This handicap has been overcome in some models by using a double action piston running in a closed cylinder having two compression chambers. On the upward stroke air is admitted to the lower chamber, and when the ignited fuel in the upper compartment forces the piston down, it compresses the air

THE DIESEL ENGINE DOES HEAVY JOBS
A Diesel-electric locomotive employed in lumbering.

in the lower chamber where another ignition occurs in the fuel injected there. Double-acting Diesels of both the four- and two-stroke cycle are in commercial use.

A modification of the "full" Diesel engine has appeared, known as the semi-Diesel. This variant has a carburetor and an electric ignition system which operates to start the engine. After the "warming-up" process is completed, the carburetor and ignition are automatically shut off, fuel oil is injected into the compression chambers, and the engine continues its operation as a "full" Diesel. An air pressure of from 275 to 325 pounds per square inch is used in the compression chamber of the semi-Diesel. This type of Diesel can be used with advantage on tractors, busses, trucks, small boats, and even airplanes.

HAIR-SPLITTING PRECISION

Modern metallurgy has come to the rescue of this efficient and economical engine by furnishing strong, light alloys to take the place of heavy parts necessary to withstand high pressures.

Courtesy International Harvester Co.

THE ECONOMY AND POWER OF THE DIESEL HAS RESULTED IN ITS USE
IN TRACTORS FOR MANY PURPOSES

Courtesy Hercules Motors Corp.

A DIESEL-POWERED TRUCK

Used extensively in submarines during the World War, the Diesel has found wider application in transportation because of the reduction in weight and size.

Precision is required in manufacturing the parts of modern machines. This fact is especially noticeable in producing the plungers used in the fuel injection pumps on Diesels. After the nitralloy steel plungers have been made by an automatic machine, twenty-five different operations are necessary to perfect them. They must be accurate to within a quarter of one ten-thousandth of an inch (0.000025)—about one-hundredth of the diameter of a human hair! These close limits and the extreme care taken throughout the manufacture of the pumps assure an accurate division of the fuel into minute particles and an equally accurate injection of each of these particles into the combustion chamber at precisely the right time. No packing is required in a pump made to such standards.

Nitralloy steel is used by a well-known implement company in making the plungers, bushings, and valves. These parts are given a hardness that is about seventy-five per cent greater than that of tool steels. This result is obtained by sealing the parts in an accurately controlled electric furnace for thirty-six hours while ammonia gas circulates throughout the furnace. The nitrogen in the ammonia reacts to the surface of the steel to form iron nitrides which become very hard and immune to corrosion.

HEART OF THE STREAMLINER

Huge Diesels with many cylinders have long been in use to run generators in electric power stations. The spectacular streamlined trains of the last few years have turned more and more to Diesel-electric locomotives. This modern "iron horse" carries several Diesels to drive generators which furnish electricity for the driving motors. In August, 1935, a railroad operating out of Chicago was the first to use a Diesel-electric locomotive to haul a passenger train. This engine developed 1,800 horsepower and proved its worth in rigorous trials. In June, 1937, the same railroad ran a train from Cincinnati to Washington, D. C., a distance of about 550 miles, for the longest non-stop run ever made by a

Courtesy Union Pacific Railroad

A FAST STREAMLINED TRAIN HAULED BY A GREAT DIESEL
POWER PLANT ON WHEELS

train east of the Mississippi River. The locomotive is built in two units, each of which has two-cylindered Diesels. The overall length of the multiple unit is 138 feet, and it weighs 570,000 pounds, including 2,200 gallons of water and 2,400 gallons of oil. Another railroad, well in the van of progress, put an even greater Diesel-engined passenger locomotive into service in December, 1937. Running between Chicago and Los Angeles in a little less than forty hours, this seventeen-car train is the largest streamliner in the world. Capable of developing speeds in excess of 110 miles per hour, the new Diesel locomotive is actually three cars, each of which houses two 900-horsepower synchronized Diesel engines delivering a total of 5,400 horsepower. Control of the entire plant centers in the cab which is in the nose of the first car. The multiple unit is more than 209 feet long. Each of the six Diesels is directly connected to generators which provide electricity for the two traction motors mounted on each of the six trucks.

Rudolf Diesel lies in his ocean tomb, almost forgotten; but thousands of machines bear the name he made illustrious. On farm and highway, railroad and ocean, are testimonials to his genius. Many scientists, engineers, and industrialists have devoted their skill and ability to making the Diesel engine one of the most important contributions to modern invention.

T HE FIRST AMERICAN SUBMARINE that stood a practical test and was the prototype of the modern U-boat was the *Holland,* named after John P. Holland, its designer and builder. It was tested in the lower bay of New York harbor before the United States Naval Board of Inspection and Survey on November 12, 1898. A torpedo was discharged under water, and the vessel went through a program of diving and running at full speed and reversing while submerged. In 1901 the *Fulton,* a vessel of similar construction, was officially tested and its crew remained submerged for fifteen hours without suffering any inconvenience.

The modern submarine can safely dive to a depth of two hundred feet. Its hull is divided into water-tight compartments and it carries water ballast and fuel oil tanks. While running on the surface the boat uses gasoline or Diesel engines. Propulsion below the surface is effected through electric storage batteries. Vision is afforded by two or three periscopes. Used chiefly as a tool of war, the submarine is equipped to fire torpedoes from tubes in the bow and stern. On the deck of the craft a variety of guns may be placed, such as light cannon, machine guns, and anti-aircraft guns, which, of course, are usable only when the ship is on the surface.

ITS ROLE DURING THE WAR

During the World War the German U-boat became the terror of the seas, and, after the sinking of the *Lusitania* with the loss of many lives, the Germans sank 4,118 enemy vessels and 1,390 neutral vessels to prevent supplies from reaching the Allies. Against the menace of the German undersea boats, the Allies developed camouflage, sent out opposing submarines and destroyers and provided their merchantmen with naval guns for protection, so that by September, 1917, Germany's submarine warfare was much weakened. The entire world lost more than fifteen

Courtesy U. S. Navy Recruiting Bureau

U.S.S. *BONITA*, A "V" TYPE SUBMARINE

million tons of shipping during the World War as a result of submarine activity.

Since the World War the increase of the number of submarines has been rapid. Most of these were built for purposes of war, although some use has been made of them for scientific undersea exploration. Several devices have been developed that permit crews to escape from submarines disabled below the surface. The leading nations are continually making bigger, faster, and more formidable submarines.

Yet, while the effectiveness of the submarine as a weapon in time of war increased, submarine defenses have been developed even faster. By means of sounding devices on board surface ships the approach of submarines can easily be detected. Large areas of sea and channels can be protected by steel nets. Merchant vessels can readily be equipped with anti-submarine guns. It is extremely dangerous for submarines to approach battleships or cruisers,

A GERMAN SUBMARINE DURING DIVING EXERCISES IN THE BAY OF KIEL

whenever these are protected by torpedo boats. Moreover, the hulls of modern war ships are strong and thick and in addition may be protected by steel nets, making them nearly immune from attack. Thus, today, the role that the submarine will play in the next war is again in doubt and dispute.

IT IS HARD to realize that our large cities could not have the impressive skyline and the towering steel structures, such as the Empire State Building in New York and the Board of Trade Building in Chicago, if it were not for the modern electric elevator.

The first platform lifts appeared about the middle of the eighteenth century as crude hoists in mines or in freight warehouses. They were generally operated by spur-geared machinery and powered by steam. Freight elevators for stores and office buildings appeared about the same time. Henry Waterman of New York built a crude one for a two-story structure; while George H. Fox and Company of Boston began to manufacture a similar type of platform lift by the early fifties.

It remained for Elisha Graves Otis to build elevators on a successful commercial scale as early as 1852 in Yonkers, New York. Two years later, he introduced a safety mechanism which would automatically stop the platform from plunging to the bottom should the cable break. Otis is also responsible for the introduction of the first successful passenger elevator in 1857 in New York City. It was powered by steam, as was also the first one installed in an office building in 1869.

Hydraulic lifts appeared in Europe about 1860. They consisted of a plunger or piston which ran in a hydraulic cylinder anchored securely in the ground. This type of elevator was gradually used in both Europe and America for both passengers and freight. It was largely superseded in 1878 by the vertical-cylinder hydraulic machine introduced by Cyrus W. Baldwin. An automatic valve adjusted the varying amounts of water pressure, controlling the movement of the piston, which in turn was operated by a special lever in the car.

Courtesy Otis Elevator Co.
AN EARLY STEAM ELEVATOR
The crude platform is equipped with the old safety device.

People considered as a marvelous performance the raising of this hydraulic lift to a height of ten or twelve stories at a speed of from four to eight hundred feet a minute. With the improved efficiency of this device, came the opening of the steel-framed skyscraper era.

ELECTRICALLY-OPERATED ELEVATORS

The supremacy of the hydraulic type of elevator was not seriously threatened until 1889, when Otis Brothers and Company constructed the first successful electric hoist. Cables, wound around a drum powered by an electric motor through a spur-

Courtesy Otis Elevator Co.

THE FIRST SAFETY ELEVATOR
This old drawing shows the operation of the safety. When Elisha Otis tested this device
in 1853, he cried "All safe" when the rope was cut and the safeties took hold.

gear mechanism, raised and lowered the car. Before long, an automatic switch and push button took the place of the hand-operated
moving control rope.

As the automatic operating devices appeared, doing away with
the need of an attendant, these electric elevators became popular
in private homes and in apartment buildings. They gradually took
the place of the hydraulic lift, for the necessary machine occupied
less space and was much more simple to operate.

With the extension skyward of the city office building to
twenty, thirty and forty floors, an even more efficient type of

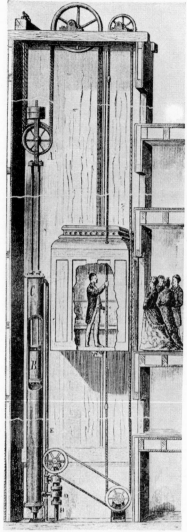

THE HYDRAULIC ELEVATOR
This old drawing depicts one of the first
geared hydraulic elevators operated by a
hand rope in the car.

elevator was needed. This demand was met in 1904 by the Otis Company in the introduction of the first gearless or direct-traction machine. The basis of its operation was a slow-speed motor of great efficiency, with pliable steel cables running on two grooved driving pulleys; from there they extended to the huge iron balances or counter-weights which we frequently see today moving up and down on their track in the rear of the shaft. This counterweight balances the loaded elevator car, hence the motor has only to overcome friction and the slight differences caused by the varying weights of the loads. Sometimes you will see steel cables attached to the bottom of the elevator car. These tend to equalize the weight of the cables between the elevator and the counter-balance. It is interesting to note that each one of these steel ropes is strong enough to hold the car alone.

IMPROVEMENTS IN ELECTRIC ELEVATORS

The many improvements of recent years in the electrical elevator have increased its efficiency and safety many fold.

Courtesy Otis Elevator Co.
THE FIRST SUCCESSFUL ELECTRIC ELEVATOR
This machine was used for freight purposes for thirty years until the building
was demolished in 1919.

One of the most interesting ones is the photoelectric self-leveling platform which automatically stops at each floor, thus conserving time, power, and wear and tear on machinery. Another late invention, which intrigues us as we wait in front of the elevator door, is the intricate flash system, indicating the location of each car. Other signal mechanisms controlled by push buttons, both in the car and by waiting passengers, also materially facilitate elevator service.

The latest development in control operation is known as "highest call return," whereby each car automatically reverses its direction of travel at the highest floor where a call has been registered, thus saving the time of an unnecessary trip to the top of the hatchway when there are no waiting passengers.

A most unusual elevator installation and the only one of its kind in use is that of eight double deck Otis signal control elevators in the Sixty Wall Tower Building, New York. These elevators have two plaforms contained in one carframe, the upper platforms stopping at the even numbered floors and the lower platforms at the odd-numbered floors, or vice-versa. The platforms have an attendant and a bank of operating buttons, and are interconnected as are the doors, so that the elevator cannot start until both platform doors are closed. The elevator is thus enabled to transfer passengers at two floors simultaneously, thereby saving considerable time. These eight elevators in the tower provide service equivalent to about fourteen single deck elevators and hence they make available for rental use the floor area which would otherwise be taken up on each floor of the building by six elevator hatchways. This would be a very material advantage in saving space, particularly in a tower building.

THE ANSWER TO THE PROBLEM OF THE SKYSCRAPER
The gearless traction machine, introduced shortly after the turn of the century, provided an efficient way to reach the thirtieth or fortieth floor.

A MODERN INSTALLATION

The elevator of the present day is not only a swift, safe, and silent mechanism, but it is enclosed in a fashion calculated to please the eye.

Courtesy Otis Elevator Co

Some freight elevator systems are managed by an operator at a central control switch, who receives all calls and sends the cars where needed.

Safety devices have appeared so rapidly that practically every type of possible accident has been insured against. Automatic speed governors, automatic brakes which shut off the power if excessive speed occurs, automatic stopping switches in the car, automatically-locked doors and gates, all mean added safety to the passengers. If, for some reason, these devices fail to work, and the car plunges to the bottom of the shaft, spring and compressed oil buffers prevent serious accidents. This almost never hap-

Courtesy Otis Elevator Co.
THIS MACHINE OPERATES THE DOUBLE-DECKER
The double-deck elevators installed in one of New York's towers are
powered by this development of the gearless machine.

pens; in fact, statistics show that the elevators in New York City have one fatal mishap for every 196,000,000 passengers carried.

In order to facilitate further the use of buildings over twenty or thirty stories, a system of express elevators takes office workers directly from the first floor to the thirtieth or fortieth; while some cars in such buildings as the R. C. A. and Empire State in New York City do not stop until the fiftieth or even the seventieth stories.

Interesting figures quite typical of other modern structures are available on the R. C. A. Building elevator system. Their cars travel at a rate of fifteen miles per hour, and speed from the first to the sixty-fifth floor in thirty-nine seconds, while from 8 A.M. until 6:30 P.M. they cover a span equal to 2100 miles—the distance from New York City to the Grand Canyon in Arizona.

In New York City alone there are over 41,000 elevators, which travel 100,000 miles a day, carrying more passengers than all the other transportation facilities of the metropolitan area combined.

CONTRIBUTIONS OF ELEVATOR TO MODERN CITY

Thus the electric elevator has made possible the concentration of large business interests and population in a small area, for a whole commercial organization with its several thousand employes may be located in one skyscraper. This situation has had much to do with determining real estate values and the rate of property returns.

By making even the higher floors accessible, the elevator has made better light and air conditions possible for countless city dwellers and office workers, who otherwise would have to live in shadow and dust.

Perhaps, no other one single modern city convenience has influenced the size, appearance, wealth, and congestion of our metropolitan areas as has the electric elevator.

ESCALATORS

Very similar in purpose to the elevator, is the electrically operated escalator or inclined moving stairway, used for both passengers and freight service. This consists of a series of small treads or platforms resembling ordinary stairs, carried on an endless chain, which become horizontal as they advance upward on the incline. They move so slowly and fit the entrance and exit platforms on each floor so nicely that even the less agile person has no difficulty in getting on or off them. A moving hand rail also adds greatly to the comfort and assurance of the passenger.

This type of lift has proved a boon to weary shoppers in department stores who find the elevators too crowded or too long in arriving. By providing continuous up and down movement, the escalator can accommodate as much freight and as many passengers as several elevators. Hence it is used extensively in freight warehouses, theaters, subways and, particularly, in department stores. Most of these escalators operate at an angle of 30°, and at a speed of about ninety feet a minute. It has not been found feasible to use them for over a sixty-foot rise, for that appears to be the limit of their operating efficiency. The escalators in the principal London underground, or subway, stations are among the fastest and longest in the world.

IMAGINE the surpise and awe that filled Columbus and his men on one of their visits to the New World when they saw the natives playing with a heavy, dark-colored ball, which bounced about queerly with lifelike antics. This, they discovered, the Indians made from a milky substance which oozed out from the trunk of particular tropical trees and plants.

More than two and a half centuries passed before any commercial use was made of this remarkable material, which the French referred to as "caoutchouc" or the Indian word for "weeping tree." It remained, however, for the ingenious English chemist, Joseph Priestly, in 1770 to give it the modern name, when he discovered that this substance would rub out pencil marks on paper. The curiosity and interest of inventive souls was further aroused by tales of returned sailors and travelers who told of the partially waterproof garments made by South American natives from the sticky product of the caoutchouc tree.

EARLY EXPERIMENTERS

The names of Thomas Hancock and Charles Mackintosh must be mentioned as pioneers in the rubber industry. The former was an enterprising business man, who attempted to manufacture and sell rubber products, such as shoes, carriage tires, and tubing. Mackintosh, a Glasgow inventor, in 1823 experimented with introducing rubber between two pieces of cloth, and pressing them together until a rubberized fabric resulted. Coats made out of this were called "mackintoshes" and even today we speak of waterproof jackets as such. Although this rubberized material was particularly useful in the misty, foggy weather of the British Isles, it could not withstand the extreme climate of the United States. In the intense heat of the American summer the rubber mixture became sticky, while in the winter it became stiff and

CHARLES GOODYEAR
The discoverer of the vulcanization process which has made rubber one of the materials most useful to man.

Paul's Photos, Chicago

useless. It remained for an American to make rubber a useful commercial product.

As early as 1820, curious Bostonians were treated to the amazing sight of crude rubber shoes, made by South American Indians. Enterprising Yankee ingenuity was aroused by the prospect of their commercial possibilities. Companies were formed, and attempts were made to manufacture rubber products, which met the same fate as Mackintosh's waterproof fabric. Cold weather made them brittle, while in summer they became sticky and gave off foul odors. People grew disgusted with rubber articles and declared them unfit for use.

GOODYEAR'S STRUGGLE

About a hundred years ago Charles Goodyear, a young Philadelphian who was a merchant and inventor, stood in front of the Roxbury India Rubber Company store in New York. Upon entering and examining a valve on a rubber life preserver, he told the manager he could improve upon it. The latter replied that unfortunately the company had failed, since manufactured rubber goods had been found impractical, but that a fortune awaited the man who could perfect a process which would prevent rubber from melting or cracking. At once Goodyear's inventive genius was aroused. He returned to Philadelphia and began experimenting.

The problem clearly was to treat crude rubber with some process or chemical which would make the finished product suitable for practical use. His kitchen was his first laboratory, and Goodyear spent hours adding one substance after another to the sticky mess on the stove.

Failing to find just the right combining material, his family penniless, he decided the next year to move to New York. Here he found friends who provided a laboratory and chemicals on credit. His wife, confident of his success, sold homespun thread and finally even her personal trinkets, so that he might continue his work.

One day Goodyear tried mixing magnesium salts with the crude rubber and heated the mixture in slacked lime. Next he molded the mass into thin sheets. At last it seemed he had found the correct combination! He hastened to patent the process, and began producing rubber goods. Rubber companies, although still dubious, showed some signs of interest.

It was discovered, however, that even mild acids made the rubber fabric sticky and impractical for use. Undaunted, Goodyear moved to Boston and continued his experiments. One day by accident he dropped some sulphuric acid on a sheet of rubber, and thus found a combination of substances which would withstand heat. Patenting this process in 1837, he again began to manufacture rubber toys, overshoes, and carriage robes on a commercial basis. The officials of the bankrupt Roxbury Rubber Company allowed him to use the company's idle machinery, although they could give no financial aid.

Goodyear was not as yet satisfied with his rubber product, and kept on with his experiments. During these months even his friends agreed with a wit's description of the inventor: "If you meet a man who has on an India rubber cap, stock, coat, vest,

Courtesy Goodyear Tire & Rubber Co.

BUD-GRAFTING RUBBER TREES IN SUMATRA

and shoes, and an India rubber money purse in his pocket, without a cent of money in it, that man is Charles Goodyear."

His attention was next drawn to the work of Nathaniel Haywood, a foreman in the defunct rubber factory, who had discovered that rubber treated with sulphur and dried in the sun did not become sticky. Goodyear bought out Haywood's patent rights in 1839 and continued his own experiments. The government had become interested in the rubber industry by this time, and ordered one hundred and fifty mail sacks. Goodyear filled the order and left the rubber sacks hanging in a display room, but upon his return some days later found the sacks in a gummy, foul-smelling mass on the floor. This process evidently was not adaptable to thick, heavy articles, and more experimenting had to be done.

Courtesy Goodyear Tire & Rubber Co.
CALENDERING MACHINE IN A TIRE FACTORY
Rubber and other essential ingredients are forced into the fabric as it
passes through the rolls.

VULCANIZATION DISCOVERED

A group of Goodyear's friends dropped in to visit him one evening. While he was showing bits of the sulphurized mixture, some accidentally fell on the stove. To his surprise the heat did not melt the stuff; instead, it became hard, only slightly charring. He placed this piece of rubber outdoors in the cold, and the next morning found it as pliable as it had been the previous evening.

Thus the principle later known as "vulcanization" was discovered! Interestingly enough this word was applied to the process by an Englishman, and had its origin in the name of the Roman fire god Vulcan. Goodyear soon found that vulcanized rubber possessed widely varying qualities of elasticity, softness, or hardness, depending on the amounts of sulphur and other chemicals added, and the length of time it was subjected to heat.

His goal was at last in sight —all that remained now was to perfect the process for commercial manufacturing. While he continued his experiments, his impoverished family was kept alive by charitable friends. Finally in 1841 he felt he had made sufficient progress

Courtesy Goodyear Tire & Rubber Co.

TAPPING A RUBBER TREE

to open a small factory in Springfield, Massachusetts, and produce sheet rubber. Three years later, he patented his discovery and with the aid of his brother-in-law, William de Forrest, opened a manufacturing plant at Naugatuck, Connecticut.

Commercially important as Goodyear's vulcanization process was, he did not realize any financial return from it, for he was obliged to grant manufacturing licenses for a mere pittance and reduce royalty percentages to almost nothing. He did very little manufacturing himself, preferring to continue his experiments in making various household articles and wearing apparel. The notebook he kept during these days shows many sketches of life-preservers (his particular hobby), sails, umbrellas, overshoes for horses to use on slippery streets, tents, air mattresses, and floor coverings. For the business man he suggested a rubber hat with an invisible pocket for papers, while for the ocean traveler he proposed a rubber jacket which might be inflated in case of a shipwreck.

In spite of repeated discouragements and utter failures, Goodyear never lost his love of public acclaim. To gain renown in England and to forestall the effect of an English patent issued in 1843 for a vulcanizing process, he constructed an elaborate display for the great International Exhibition held in London in 1851. The exhibit, which cost $30,000, contained a number of rooms built of hard rubber and furnished with rubber furniture, musical instruments, and carpets. For this effort, he was rewarded with the Grand Council Medal. At the Exposition in Paris in 1855, he also exhibited an elaborate display of rubber furniture, caskets, and jewelry, receiving the cross of the Legion of Honor for its excellence.

His return to Amercia in 1858 brought about a temporary adjustment in his financial and patent affairs, but as usual it did not last long. Charles Goodyear—as is so often the case with the world's greatest benefactors—died heavily in debt in 1860 in the sixtieth year of his life. Before his passing, however, he saw his vulcanized product put to over five hundred uses, rubber factories established employing thousands of persons, and the United States alone producing rubber goods worth $8,000,000.

For some reason or other, Goodyear did not apply his experiments to the rubber tire. This was done by an Englishman, Robert W. Thompson, who in 1845 invented and patented a pneumatic carriage tire, consisting of five-inch vulcanized hollow belting, formed from several thicknesses of rubber. Although his tires were durable, they were not used to any extent and were considered a freak invention.

It was not until forty years later, however, that John Boyd Dunlop, a veterinary surgeon of Belfast, made an air tire for his son's tricycle, based on the modern pneumatic principle. He patented this process in 1888, and two years later began to manufacture and market his product so successfully that he had branches throughout the world.

The introduction of cord fabric in 1910 increased the life of the tire casing immeasurably and led to experiments for making tread compounds of comparable wearing qualities.

EXTENT OF RUBBER PLANTATION INDUSTRY

The moist, tropical regions of South America, the West Indies, Africa, and the Indo-Malay peninsula produce crude rubber. Until about 1900, most of the commercial rubber came from the Amazon area of South America and from the African Congo. At present the world's rubber supply comes principally from Ceylon, the Dutch East Indies, and British Malaya; while small amounts come from Liberia, Brazil, India, and the Philippines.

The Far Eastern rubber plantation industry is largely the result of the work of Sir Henry Wickham, an English botanist, who experimented with 70,000 rubber tree seeds which he brought back from Brazil. These seeds were planted in the Royal Botanical Gardens, and later the plants were sent to Ceylon, Java, Borneo and other East Indies. Rubber culture developed slowly, but in 1905 Brazil attempted to monopolize the world's rubber supply. Prices rose skyward and the few Eastern rubber plantation owners became so wealthy that ten years later over 3,000,000 acres in that area were planted to rubber trees.

GATHERING SAP

Courtesy B. F. Goodrich Co.

WASHING RUBBER FOR TIRES

Crude rubber contains many foreign substances. In this machine it is sprayed
with water as it passes through close-set rolls which chew the rubber and
expose many surfaces for cleaning.

In recent years American tire companies have developed rubber plantations in Liberia, Sumatra, and Malaya, while Henry
Ford is experimenting with rubber culture in Brazil on a huge
6,000,000 acre tract. It is a long, tedious process to develop a
productive plantation, for a rubber tree started from seed cannot
be tapped for five years, and ten years must elapse before it reaches
full bearing.

THE LATEX AND THE TIRE

Rubber trees are tapped much as Vermont farmers tap their maple trees. The sap is caught in small cups placed under the cut. Native laborers gather this sap or latex and pour it into large flat dishes. A solution of acetic acid is added to make the rubber globules coagulate. These particles are then run through into rollers and come out in the form of thin corrugated sheets which are dried for three weeks. Some crude rubber is dried by smoking it from ten to fourteen days. Recently liquid latex has been shipped in tank boats to the United States.

Since the automobile has become so common, about eighty per cent of the world's rubber supply has gone into tires, tubes, and various motor accessories.

The present tire manufacturing center of the United States is located in Ohio, and more particularly in the city of Akron. In the modern tire factory the sheets of crude rubber are shredded and combined with water until the mixture is pliable. Then sulphur and various chemicals are added, and the mixing process continues. The compound is now ready for the calender machine, which consists of three hollow heated cylinders. Several processes may be performed by this machine: the mixture may be rolled into sheets of various thicknesses, a layer of rubber may be laid on cloth, or ground into fabrics, so that every fiber is completely rubberized.

As much as thirty per cent of carbon black is added to the mixture used for making tire tread, to increase its abrasive resistance. To construct a tire casing, bias pieces of rubberized fabrics are stretched on an iron drum. The clincher section, known as the bead, is placed on each side and rolled out. Then the side wall and tread are added, the drum removed, an air bag inserted, and the casing placed in a pattern mold to produce the "non-skid" tread.

Vulcanization comes next. The tire is placed in tightly sealed vulcanizers, under live steam pressure from one to four hours.

Calendered rubber is also used in the manufacture of inner tubes. Strips of it are wound around a steel core, the ends being bound with cotton tape to prevent leaking, in the hot water curing process. Valves are then inserted and the ends lapped and vulcanized.

OTHER RUBBER PRODUCTS

Besides its use in the tire and tube industry, calendered rubber is utilized in the manufacturing of water bottles, rubber heels, rubber bands, hose, and belting. Air-brake hose, fruit jar rings, boots and shoes are vulcanized by forcing the calendered rubber compound through a heated iron cylinder mold.

Soft-rubber mixtures may be dissolved in gasoline or turpentine to form cements. Their principal uses are found in waterproofing fabrics, and in making molded dipped goods such as surgeons' and household gloves.

Hard rubber, made by adding greater amounts of sulphur, resists all but a few acids and gases. It is widely used for automobile batteries, telephone receivers, storage tanks, and sometimes for street pavements.

In an effort to destroy the Far Eastern monopoly of the rubber production, some successful experiments have been carried on to produce synthetic rubber, both from plants and by synthetic chemistry. This new rubber product has many qualities superior to ordinary rubber, in its greater resistance to oils, acids, and heat.

It is doubtful if any other industrial product has as extensive applications in every phase of human existence. Literally its uses span man's life from the cradle to the grave. From the baby's bottle nipple, the teething ring, and rattle to the artificial teeth, hot-water bag and air mattress that give comfort to the older person's last years, rubber plays a significant role. In fact, every hour of the day, rubber heels, rubber gloves, waterproof footwear, and garments protect man's safety and health.

The housewife has innumerable uses for it from her kitchen to the bathroom, in the indispensable rubber mats, sponges, chair and table pads, casters, fruit-jar rings, knife-handles, tubing, clothes wringer, rubber gloves, and countless other items.

What is more useful to the business man than the eraser, the typewriter roller, the noiseless business machine, the rubber band, and the mouthpiece of telephones, or even his pipestem?

The nonconducting properties of rubber have made it a vital part of the electrical industry. No better insulator has been found for wires, cables, batteries, and dynamos.

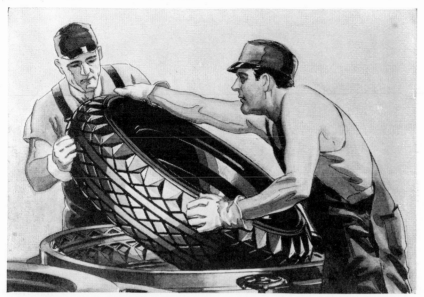

Courtesy Goodyear Tire & Rubber Co.

PATTERN MOLD WHICH PRODUCES "NON-SKID" SURFACE

In the industrial world, rubber is utilized so extensively that it is impossible more than to mention a few of its uses, such as: belting for machinery, floorings, fire hose, tires, tubing, cements, waterproof fabrics, packings and mountings for engines, doors, and windows.

The United States ranks first in the rubber industry, with Great Britain, Japan, Germany, and France, following in the order named. In fact, the annual value of the rubber products in the United States has risen in one hundred years from a few thousand dollars to one billion dollars.

PERHAPS FROM THE OLD WINE PRESS

PRINTING, the quantity reproduction of books, newspapers, magazines, and the like, is important economically and even more significant socially. The spread of learning and civilization which began with the Renaissance and has continuously increased since that time is due in no small measure to the development of printing processes. The Chinese invented printing, as well as paper, utilizing movable type a half century before it was used in Europe.

However, the invention of printing in Europe was almost certainly an independent occurrence; the renowned Johann Gutenberg, of Mainz, is generally credited with the invention. Perhaps

A PORTION OF A MANUSCRIPT SHOWING TYPE OF BOOK USED
BEFORE PRINTING WAS INVENTED

GUTENBERG TAKING THE FIRST PROOF
(From an old print.)

taking his idea from the old wine press, Gutenberg was printing with movable type before 1456. The first products of printing presses were papal indulgences, but the first book which has been preserved was undoubtedly made in or before that year. This was the Mazarin Bible, the work of several men working with Gutenberg; but the fact that none of these men—Johann Fust, Peter Schoeffer, or any of the others—ever claimed the invention, even after Gutenberg's death, indicates perhaps that his origination of printing was accepted at the time. The first dated book was a psalter produced in 1457 by Fust and Schoeffer; it was in many ways typical of the books of the period. In appearance it closely resembled the handmade books of the medieval monks. The type was cut to resemble the heavy gothic script in which they wrote, and the illumination of initial letters and the use of color throughout showed little change in style from the earlier unprinted works.

POCKET EDITIONS

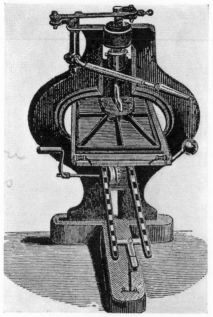

FIRST IRON FRAME PRESS
Devised by the Earl of Stanhope in 1798, this press had a frame of cast iron and an improved screw-and-lever operating mechanism.

From the original centers of Mainz and Strasbourg printing spread rapidly over Europe; so that by the beginning of the sixteenth century about twelve million volumes had already been published. Venice became the focus of printing activity, and the spirit of the Renaissance was manifested in the work of such pioneers as Nicolas Jenson, a Frenchman, who made popular the use of roman type faces, copied from old Roman inscriptions. These clear simple styles began to supplant the illegible gothic and are the basis of nearly all modern type faces. Another immortal Venetian innovator was Aldus Manutius, who in addition to creating italic type was probably the first to glimpse and capitalize on the commercial possibilities of the new art. In the twenty years after 1495 he published quantities of cheap editions of the classics, judiciously printing them in small, readily marketable volumes. Other type designers of the fifteenth and later centuries included Garamond, Granjon, Van Dyck, Caslon, Baskerville, Bodoni, and the modern American genius, Frederic Goudy.

The first book printed in the English language was paradoxically not printed in England; it was made in 1475 in France by William Caxton, who after learning the printing art on the Continent returned to his own country and began the English development of printing. Printing was brought to America in the first quarter of the sixteenth century; it was used in Mexico City where the Catholic missionaries were translating religious documents

FLAT-BED AND PLATEN HAND PRESS, 1829

into the languages of the Indians. The first press in the territory which was to become the United States was set up in Cambridge, Massachusetts, by Stephen Day in 1639.

SHRDLU ETAOIN

Type, which is the chief distinguishing characteristic of printing, is cast from a compound of lead, tin, and antimony, their proportions varying as the metal is used for linotype, monotype, or handset. All printing devices such as type, engraving, woodcuts, and the like are "type high," that is, of a uniform height from base to printing surface of .918 inches. The size of letter faces is graduated in a standardized system of "points"; there are seventy-two points to the inch, and twelve points are called a pica. Commonly used sizes range from the six-point, one which is very small and is used in newspaper want-ads and the like, to such large sizes as those used in newspaper headlines and posters. This book is set in twelve-point type.

For centuries the only typesetting device was handset, which is done by hand with a tray called a composing stick into which the letters are fitted one by one. With the coming of such inven-

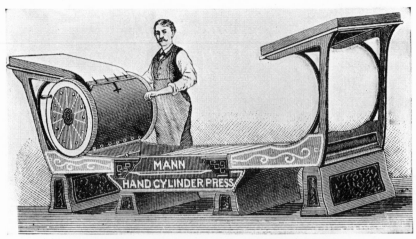

AN EARLY TYPE OF HAND CYLINDER PRESS

tions as high-speed rotary presses using stereotype plates and print-ing on continuously unwinding rolls of machine-made paper, the only obstacle to rapid printing was the slowness of the hand compositors. The nineteenth century saw the appearance of in-vention after invention to accelerate the typesetting process. Some of these actually attempted to assemble the type from variously shaped cases; others facilitated the distribution of type after it had been used. None was effective, and the compositor came to the printshop early and worked late while the pressman in a few minutes ran off all that could be set up and waited help-lessly for more. At last, after several years of futile experiment with the older ideas in compositing machinery, Ottmar Mergen-thaler brought forth his linotype. This long awaited invention revolutionized the printing industry. It was first used com-mercially in 1886, and its adoption spread rapidly. Here was a machine which quickly cast type, a whole line at a time; it was a time-saving device which made possible an enormous expansion in the size and quantity of all sorts of printed matter.

The machine, with the many improvements which have been added, is exceedingly complex, combining the functions of letter selection, line arrangement, and the casting of the slug. Although the actual arrangement of letters is different, the linotype operator uses a keyboard similar to that of a typewriter. The familiar, mysterious words, "shrdlu" and "etaoin," seen often in broken lines of newspaper copy are merely the two left hand columns of letter keys, down which the linotyper drags a finger when he has made a mistake and wishes to fill out the line slug. The striking of a letter on the keyboard drops a metal pattern of the letter from its magazine into an assembly frame. When all the letters and spaces are in place, the wedges are pressed down between words so that the line is filled accurately. Molten type alloy is then poured into the mold, where it is shaped by the pattern faces. The slug is then cooled and placed in a long tray called a galley.

The typograph and the intertype are two similar machines; the monotype acts on corresponding principles but casts a line of

Courtesy The Intertype Corporation

THE INTERTYPE MACHINE

Courtesy Lanston Monotype Machine Co.

A MONOTYPE KEYBOARD

Holes are punched in a paper ribbon through the operation
of this keyboard. The ribbon is then placed in the casting
machine (not shown), and the position of the holes determines the characters to be cast into type.

single letters. After galley proofs are pulled by hand in a simple,
cylinder press, the long mass of type in the galley is cut into page
lengths and, surrounded by wooden blocks of "furniture," is
locked in the "chase," a metal frame, held securely by double
wedges called "quoins," which are tightened with a turn-screw.
This is then called a form and after it has been "made ready," that
is, meticulously leveled in the bed of the press, it is ready for
printing.

STEEL JAWS AND LEAD TEETH

The earliest printing was done with a clumsy screw-press in
which a vertical, threaded rod with a flat piece at its lower end

RICHARD HOE

was turned through a frame against the body of type beneath. By the early part of the nineteenth century, however, George Clymer in Philadelphia was operating a press run with a set of integrated levers, and presses powered by toggle-jointed bars, like those of a stone crusher, were developed about this time. In 1810 Friedrich König, a German, attempted the application of steam to the machine, and thus printing presses began to approach their modern efficiency. König's invention was used on a press of the flat-bed type; a cylinder rolled across the level type surface to produce the impression. The prototype of the great modern rotary presses was a press invented by Richard Hoe, completed in 1847, in which the body of type was fastened into the curved bed in the cylinder, and the impression was made, a sheet at a time, by contact with other rollers. The process was improved by the invention of a press which for the first time utilized a continuous roll of paper, automatically fed and machine-cut into lengths as desired. This press, invented in 1865 by William Bullock, was also the first to print simultaneously on both sides of the paper.

The paper roll was the product of a much earlier invention made by Louis Robert in 1798, but usually credited to Henry Fourdrinier, who introduced the paper-making machine into England in 1803. The idea, however, had lain dormant until a press was devised which could make use of it. One of the last great steps in the actual press processes was taken when the Walter press was patented in England. This innovation, used instead of a form of type, which was hard to work with and constantly in danger of breaking up into "pi," curved stereotypes, cast from the type in one piece, which fitted around the cylinder bed. The improve-

HUGE ROTARY PRESS USED IN MAGAZINE AND LARGE-SCALE
BOOK PRODUCTION

A MODERN NEWSPAPER PRESS

ments in flat-bed presses were climaxed in the invention in 1883 by Robert Miehle of the press which still bears his name.

In the modern world of publishing most magazines and practically all newspapers are printed on rotary presses; most books, on the other hand, are printed on flat-bed presses, which are of two principal kinds. One is the cylinder press, in which the type bed is horizontal and slides back and forth in grooves, passing successively beneath inking rollers and the cylinder which makes the impression of the type on the paper. The other type is the platen press; in it the type bed is vertical, and against it a second plate, hinged to the type bed like a jaw, exerts the pressure to imprint the type matter. The jaws rhythmically open and close, and when they are apart the ink rollers dart down across the type surface and back again.

The mighty rotary presses are among the most imposingly complicated machines in the entire world. Around the massive cylinders are the complex curved surfaces of the stereotype plates, across which the unrolling paper is propelled, impression being made against other cylinders. Rotaries are sometimes used for printing on single sheets, but the famous newspaper and magazine giants consume great rolls of paper, which unwind continuously as they pass between pair after pair of the mighty rollers. With the development of these high-speed reproductive techniques came the subordinate but necessary invention of machines for mechanical feeding and guiding of the paper stock, and for drying the impression and cutting and folding the finished printed matter.

WHEN A "FLONG" IS DRIED

Two of the sweeping achievements which have helped make possible the tremendous volume of modern printing were the inventions of the stereotype and the electrotype processes. Although its great vogue did not come until considerably later, the method of the stereotype was invented in 1725 by William Ged, a Scot. Like many another inventor, Ged died broken-hearted and penniless, his work destroyed by jealous compositors and his ideas failing to obtain any sort of acceptance. The stereo technique was given its name by Firmin Didot, a member of the illustrious French publishing family, who improved and popularized the process.

The purpose of the stereotype is to reproduce a mass of type in the form of a single metal plate. In the accomplishment of this, the form of type is covered with a "flong," made of alternate layers of blotting and tissue paper, which is pressed against the type surface, so that an impression is made in the damp, flexible material. The flong is then dried on the type, and when it is removed it is called a matrix, or mat—a mold into which the liquid metal is poured. When the metal is partially cooled, the mat is removed and the stereotype is mounted, type high, on a wood base, if it is to be used in a flat-bed press. If it is to be printed on a rotary, the plate is curved to fit the cylinder. Other processes have been invented in which the sterotype is dried in a platen-like press.

The other process, that of electrotyping, has the same purpose, but it is at once more accurate and more expensive. A mold is made from the original type matter, in wax or more recently in lead, and by an electrolytic process a thin shell of copper, or less frequently nickel or chromium, is deposited on it. The electrolyte is usually copper sulphate, which is made to break up into two elements: copper, which is spread over the mold, which serves as the cathode pole; and sulphur, which is attracted by electrolysis toward the positive pole. This pole is made of copper, and the

PRINTSHOP
From a Copper Plate, Vienna, 1805.

sulphur as it comes in contact with it forms more copper sulphate; the process is continued until the mold is covered with the desired depth of metal. The shell is then filled, in its concave back, with softer metal until it is type-high. United States currency plates are plated with chromium because this hard metal gives long wear and sharp impressions.

ZINC VERSUS COPPER

The reproduction process for printing pictures, drawings, paintings, photographs and the like, is called engraving. In modern commercial practice there are two principal kinds: line engraving,

which is done on zinc plates; and half-tone work, which is made
on copper. When there are no shadings in a picture between black
and white, as in a cartoon or other line drawing, zinc plates are
used. The drawing is photographed on the sensitized plates and
then etched chemically. If on the other hand there are many
color values, as there are in photographs, half-tone methods are
used. The picture is photographed through a ruled glass screen,
and the negative is then printed on a chemically treated copper
plate. The fineness of the screen, which ranges from sixty to
several hundred lines to the inch, depends on the degree of accuracy desired in the reproduction; it also depends on the sort of
paper on which the engraving is to be printed. Newsprint, for
example, is coarse, absorbent paper, and in making newspaper
pictures a wide screen is used. The function of the screen is to
break up the pictures into a great many dots, so that chemical
action according to the frequency of distribution of the dots can
produce gradings in value in the reproduction.

Color printing can be done from either zinc or copper engraving, but color half-tones are more widely used because of
their greater accuracy in the presentation of the original. Four
plates are made, one for each of the primary colors used in printing—yellow, red, blue, and black. The original picture is photographed through three successive color filters, so that each plate
includes the values of only one color. The finished engravings are
printed in the order given above, and the various values of each
primary color allow an endless variety of intermediate colors when
combined.

THE SUNDAY SUPPLEMENT

In addition to the kind of printing which has been discussed
above, and which is by far the most generally used, there are two
other distinctive methods, called intaglio and lithograph. Instead
of having raised surfaces, intaglio plates are characterized by an
incised design, like an etching or steel engraving, which is lower
than the surface of the plate. The surface is inked and then wiped
clean, so that the ink remains only in the incised pattern. From
this ink-filled hollow an impression is made, and the plate is again

THE BOOKBINDER
Woodcut by Jost Ammann, Frankfurt a.M., 1568.

cleaned. Probably the most familiar use of this process is found in
the photogravure or rotogravure sections of Sunday newspapers.
In spite of the necessity of removing the surplus ink from the
smooth surfaces of the plates, newspaper presses can print at high
speed as many as two hundred thousand impressions from a single
cylinder.

The other type of printing, sometimes called chemical printing, is represented by lithography, a technique invented in 1789
by Aloys Senefelder, a Bohemian. He had been trying to learn
the art of etching copper engravings, practicing the art of writing

backwards, but copper plates were expensive, and he considered practicing on a stone which he had on hand on which to grind ink. By chance, he wrote in ink a list on the stone and conceived the idea of printing directly from it. He treated the stone with a solution of nitric acid which was resistant to his greasy ink, inked the stone, and secured the first lithographic impression in the world. In modern lithography a drawing on calcareous stone, such as limestone, is made with a lithograph ink or crayon. The stone has the property of absorbing this greasy substance, and the surface is next coated with a solution of acid, gum, and water. The ink, which is then applied, tends to be repelled, because of its own greasy texture, by the water and gum and to seek the inky portions of the surface. The impression on paper is then made from a perfectly smooth surface—a process unlike either intaglio or raised-type printing. Metal plates have been extensively used in the process recently, because of their easier portability.

FIRST PRINTING
TRADE EMBLEM OF
FUST AND SCHOEF-
FER (1457)

I F YOU COULD go back a hundred years in time and tell your great-grandfather's friends about the invention and advantages of the typewriter, they probably would not inform you that the machine was impossible, as they might likely say of the airplane. The typewriter involves no basic principle with which they were unfamiliar. But they would almost certainly argue that the machine could never equal the beauty and precision of printing or the speed and accuracy of script. If you were able to convince them of the relative fallacies in these contentions—and it would not be easy—their rebuttal would likely take the line that the typewriter could never achieve the sanction of business and social usage. Men of your great-grandfather's time were practiced and graceful penmen. They would stand by that statement.

No lack of scientific knowledge or mechanical ability delayed the invention of the typewriter until the end of the last century. The art of printing and the use of individual type-letters were already matters of history; a practical, swift-acting keyboard was part of every piano. Even the specific idea was not lacking; several men had planned and even built crude "writing machines." The typewriter lagged behind because of the unconscious opposition of a social usage that clings, among other things, to a clumsy system of weights and measures. Occasionally men were willing to prophesy a great future for the instrument, but few were eager to spend the years necessary to perfect its novel form and parts. And that form and those parts had to be perfected before the instrument could be offered with any chance of success to a stubborn public, before any reputable firm could be interested in its manufacture. So it was almost inevitable that the machine would be invented by a man at once sufficiently impractical to become interested in it, and sufficiently persistent to complete the project.

TYPEWRITING MACHINE OF 1856

FATHER OF THE TYPEWRITER

In 1819 Christopher L. Sholes was born in a small town in Pennsylvania. At the age of fourteen he was apprenticed to learn the art of printing at the offices of a nearby newspaper. When he grew up, he wandered out toward the West, filling all sorts of responsible positions. Sholes was in turn a compositor or printer, an editor, a member of the Wisconsin legislature, a commissioner of public works, and a postmaster. The more creative side of his nature was shown by an interest in chess-playing and poetry. He finally gravitated to Milwaukee, where he fell in with two other men destined to become inventors, Samuel Soule and Carlos Glidden; the latter eventually devised a spader that helped to revolutionize agriculture. Sholes, while running a small job-printing shop, became interested in finding a better and more accurate

THE TYPEWRITER OF 1884

device than the hand stamp for numbering such things as tickets, blank books, and ledger pages. In 1866 he and Soule invented for the purpose a small, simple machine; simple, because it required only a few keys, and had to make only one or two single numbers on each piece of cardboard; it was not very swift in operation, nor was it meant to be. Nevertheless, it had the essential feature of a typewriter: individual keys that successively struck and left impressions of figures on paper. When Sholes showed it to Glidden, he thought for a while and then asked: "If it can write numbers, why not letters?"

Once Sholes understood what Glidden meant, he became enthusiastic about the possibilities. Together the three men took stock of the previous work that had been done in the field. They found that two Frenchmen, Progin and Foucalt, and several Americans had all invented crude writing machines and printing machines. Many of these inventors were inspired by a desire to help the blind write in the Braille system of raised dots. They found that the sliding and revolving circular carriage for holding the paper had been used by Charles Thurber of Massachusetts; that the four-bank keyboard and ingeniously inked ribbon had been employed in a machine constructed by William Francis, of New York, in 1857. They read an article in *The Scientific American* predicting that eventually the "literary piano" would completely supplant handwriting. Knowing this much, and having served their apprenticeship at the numbering machine, they began work. As a preliminary experiment they built a machine with a single key that wrote only the letter "w." The key, which closely resembled that of a telegraph, moved a bar that struck the type upward, against a ribbon, at the under side of a piece of paper.

One by one the principal problems were solved, some by the adaptation of other devices, some by complete innovations. Most of the former typewriters had arranged their type on a circular wheel, which had to be revolved before the individual key was struck. Soule conceived of a circular set of rods converging in such a way that all would strike the paper at the same spot without preliminary adjustment. In 1868 they took out patents on the completed machine, which had something of a mongrel appearance. Its numbered keyboard still was very similar to that of a piano; the curved arm that held the ribbon suggested the phonograph. It printed only capital letters. The keys were invisible, and the operator could not see what he was writing. The keys were arranged in alphabetical order. Afterwards, using the typesetter's font as a model, Sholes set them up in such a fashion that the keys most used were easiest to manipulate.

MOVING TOWARD PERFECTION

Sholes immediately began using the first machine to write letters to his friends and acquaintances. One of these communications came into the hands of a business man named Densmore, who saw the possibilities of the device and bought his way into the

A BILLING MACHINE

partnership by paying all previous expenses. He told the inventors that their first machine was too fragile and clumsy to be of any general practical use, or even to interest a manufacturer. Footing all bills, he urged Sholes to make one new machine after another. It was a hard and exasperating task. Soule and Glidden dropped out. Densmore wisely was not satisfied with half-measures, with the praise of amateurs who wrote only infrequently and at slow speeds. He sent machine after machine out to be tested by different professionals, chief among them a young court reporter in Washington, James Clephane. Clephane was a severe critic; he gave the machines hard use, and subjected each weak part to a criticism so minute that Sholes often thought it carping and lost his temper. But Densmore drove him on. Finally, in 1872, after five years that saw the building and junking of more than fifty machines, they judged they had something good enough to interest

Courtesy Burroughs Adding Machine Co.

A BOOKKEEPING MACHINE
Essentially a typewriter, this is a specialized mechanism which handles complicated work.

men who made in large quantities machinery with interchange-able parts. They were right. The Remingtons, of Ilion, New York, were so enthusiastic that they bought the patent outright. Sholes was satisfied with $12,000. Densmore insisted on a royalty that eventually paid him a hundred times more.

CONVINCING A SKEPTICAL PUBLIC

Among instruments being offered to the public for the first time, the typewriter was one almost perfect—because it had to be. Ten years passed before it began to sell. Social usage still opposed it, and people were apt to consider typed correspondence an affront. Because there were few trained typists, many business men could not appreciate the machine's possibilities for speed. Mark Twain typed his final draft of *Tom Sawyer*, but kept the

fact a secret for fear of being annoyed with questions and com-
ments. Various sales companies tackled the problem, and went so
far as to stage a mock patent fight to get publicity. Finally, in
1882 the sales began to mount. The typewriter had been introduced to the world.

During the next few years many trained machinists became
interested and a number of improvements were made. Small as
well as capital letters were used, and the shift mechanism was introduced to reduce the number of keys. The carriage was arranged in such a way that the operator could see what he was
writing. Eventually portable machines were made.

Courtesy Remington-Rand, Inc.

ASSEMBLING TYPE BARS IN THE SEGMENTS
(Typewriter manufacture.)

A variation of the typewriter enables the operator to take down spoken words with greater rapidity than can be obtained by the use of shorthand. Similar ones write in Braille for the blind. Methods such as mimeographing have been devised to duplicate what is originally written on a typewriter. But so great is the prestige of the individually typed letter that machines have been devised to write automatically from rolls similar to those used on a player piano. Machines in which the keys merely have to be touched, a motor supplying the necessary additional energy, are in general use today. Machines sensitive to sound and capable of taking down dictation directly, would put a high premium on good diction, but they are not yet produced. One of the few things that prevent the typewriter from encroaching even further on the domain of the printing press, is its uneven right-hand margin; but this has been overcome in the new "justifying" typewriters.

Courtesy Stenotype Co.

A "SHORTHAND" TYPEWRITER

CALCULATING MACHINES

W E COUNT BY TENS. The reason for this is right at our fingertips, the ten fingertips on which primitive man enumerated his possessions, his friends, and his enemies. Imagine such a man counting the six cows he happened to own, depressing a finger for each familiar beast he saw, beginning with his right thumb; if he got as far as the little finger on his left hand, he would know they were all there; if he stopped at the little finger on his right, he would know one animal was lost or stolen. All early number systems probably have such origins. The forebears of the Romans counted by fives, by the single hand instead of the double. Still other peoples counted by twenties; apparently they threw in their toes for good measure.

Our ten fingers were not only the reason for our decimal system; they were also the primitive adding machine. If the man with the six cows had the good fortune to secure three more, he would merely depress the next three fingers, one at a time, so arriving at the trigger finger of his left hand, which at once became the sum and, if a thong were tied around it, the permanent record of the sum. However, there was an obvious limitation to this method: it could not record beyond ten. When he came to the thumb on his left hand, he was stuck. Of course, he could start over again and trust to remembering that he had already counted through once, but ancient as well as modern business men have never been very prone to trust in the unaided memory. At this difficult point some unknown genius conceived the idea of putting a pebble down in front of him for each ten fingers counted.

THE SIMPLE STEPS TO THE ABACUS

Only a few relatively simple steps were needed to perfect this primitive adding machine. The use of the fingers was eventually discarded; instead of them, a row of ten pebbles represented the

Courtesy Burroughs Adding Machine Co.

ASSEMBLING AN ADDING MACHINE IN THE FACTORY

ones, another row the tens, another the hundreds, and so on. The abacus, as it is called, found its way into almost all countries. Various objects were used instead of pebbles: buttons in grooves, sets of sticks, marks made on lined paper, wooden beads strung on rods. The medieval counting house had its abacus. It is still in general use in China, and to some extent in Russia.

Besides adding and subtracting, the abacus could multiply after a laborious fashion; for example, it could get the product of sixteen and twenty-seven by adding together sixteen twenty-sevens, one after another.

There is no historical proof that the abacus developed in precisely this fashion; the origins of the crude but accurate device are lost in the primeval shadows of antiquity. But it *did* develop in some such fashion. Obviously, it would not be considered a miracle of speed or ingenuity today. Mathematical operations could be performed no more swiftly upon it than with pencil on paper, especially after the convenient system of Arabic numerals was introduced into Europe. However, it remains the model of almost all modern calculating machines.

CONTRIBUTIONS OF PASCAL AND THOMAS

In 1642 Blaise Pascal, the famous French philosopher and scientist, built a machine that speeded up the action of the abacus. The ten pebbles in the first row, representing the digits from one to ten, became numbers on a disc. When this disc, which was operated by hand, made one complete revolution, it moved a similar disc next to it one tenth of a revolution, indicating that ten units had been counted. When the first disc had made ten successive revolutions, the second disc completed one whole revolution and began to move a third disc, which recorded the hundreds. Thus the familiar process of "carrying forward" was accomplished automatically. Moreover, for the recording of larger

Courtesy National Cash Register Co., Dayton, O.

WORKMAN ASSEMBLING A NATIONAL ACCOUNTING MACHINE

numbers, each disc could be moved independently of the first. Each was also connected by pinwheel gearing to a corresponding numbered rim, which showed through a slot the number on it; this arrangement made it possible to read at any time the sum of the numbers added up on the machine, without looking at each disc separately.

Pascal's calculating machine, efficient at simultaneously recording and adding numbers, still brought to mind the crudeness of the abacus in that it could multiply only by successive additions, each of which required a separate manipulation of the discs. In 1820 Charles Thomas, of Colmar in Alsace, built a machine that speeded up this process. Once a number was set upon it, one turn of a crank added the number to itself; in other words, multiplied it by two. Two turns were equivalent to multiplication by three, and so on up to nine. A shift mechanism permitted similar multiplications by tens, hundreds, and thousands. Another shift mechanism made subtraction and division possible.

Since then, the form of the calculating machine has been changed and improved many times. Revolving discs have been replaced by levers moving in numbered slots and by a keyboard similar to that of the typewriter. The successive turns of the crank have been made partially automatic. Nevertheless, the essential features were established by the machines of Pascal and Thomas.

Thus far we have been dwelling on their purely mathematical aspects. But mathematicians could not have built them. Their intricate shift mechanisms and cogs, their delicately fashioned stepped wheels and toothed wheels and, above all, the superb accuracy with which these parts were constructed and fitted together, cannot be disposed of by the phrase "built to order." In 1671 the German philosopher Leibnitz devised a machine that would have anticipated that of Thomas by one hundred and fifty years except for the fact that it was never accurate in operation. The essential accuracy was made possible by the creative genius of many English and Continental hand machinists, by the work of Bramah, Maudsley, Clement, and other eighteenth- and nineteenth-century artists in the tooling of metal.

Courtesy Burroughs Adding Machine Co.

NEW HIGH-SPEED BANK POSTING MACHINE

MODERN CALCULATORS

Today the many varieties of the calculating machine are all important to both business and science. Simple counting machines are familiar to anyone who rides on a streetcar and notices his fare being "rung up." The even commoner cash register, a surprisingly recent American invention, does much more than prevent dishonesty; it prints records that could otherwise be made only by a tedious clerical routine. Other combinations of the typewriter and adding machine simplify the labor of the bookkeeper. Others calculate, in a twentieth of the time formerly necessary, astronomical tables called ephemerides, logs of the heavens that give the positions of a large number of stars from day to day. Finally, as an almost incredible example of achievement in this line, there is the automatic Hollerith sorting and tabulating machine, which can compile statistics that would be impractical to seek by

THE COMPTOMETER IN USE

any other methods. Questions on a card are answered by punching holes into the card instead of writing the answers. Stacks of these cards are fed into the machine. Electrical brushes make various connections through the holes, and so operate mechanical devices that sort the cards and tabulate all the information punched in them.

The calculating machine will certainly see many startling developments in the next decades, and not all of them may be unexpected. Some may merely be the result of the commercial production of machines that have already been successfully made by hand tooling, machines that can perform even more involved mathematical operations than multiplication and division, such as the determination of logarithms. However, none of these machines will "think." Their province has been and will be to relieve man of much repetitive, monotonous, uncreative work.

THE ELECTRIC GENERATOR AND MOTOR

SISTERS UNDER THE SKIN

THE ELECTRIC generator, sometimes called the dynamo, and the electric motor are twins, born of the same electrical principle: the dynamo converts mechanical energy into electrical impulses, and the electric motor converts electrical energy into mechanical work. This pair of power-producers looms very large in the diverse activities of modern civilization. Without them radio, telephone, lighting, automobiles, airplanes, industrial furnaces, magnets, cranes, presses, and ocean liners could never have achieved their enormous efficiency and widespread use.

The principle of the electric generator was accidentally discovered in 1820 by Hans Christian Oersted, a professor in Copenhagen University, Denmark. While lecturing to his students, Oersted by chance placed an electric wire near a compass needle and was amazed to see the needle swing about. Other scientists immediately set out to discover what relationship existed to cause this action. The most valuable work of that early period was done by the French physicist and mathematician, André Ampère, for whom the practical unit of electrical current is named. Ampère was a man of gentle personality whose life was saddened by the violent death of his father in the Reign of Terror in Lyons and by the death of his wife; his capacity for intensive analytical work was tremendous. Seven days after Oersted made his famous observation, Ampère had prepared a paper explaining the phenomenon, and in following years he made a thorough and enlightening study of the field of electrodynamics and electromagnetics. Despite the clear-sighted work of Ampère, Wollaston, and others, puzzled scientists made little headway in subsequent years in explaining the action of the coil and magnet, and the tremendous practical implications were scarcely imagined.

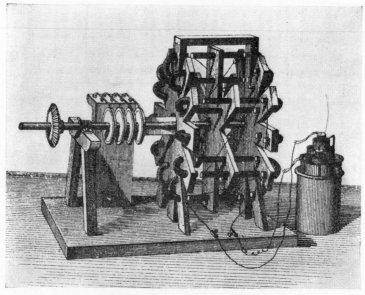

THE ELECTRIC MOTOR OF 1838

WANDERING FROM HIS TEST TUBES

However, an English chemist named Michael Faraday, lured by the fascination of electrical problems, wandered away from his test tubes and, in 1831, began his epochal work in electromagnetic induction. He found that when a magnet is thrust into a coil of wire, an electric current is induced in the wire, just as a current is induced in the wire when it is moved past a magnet. In essence this is the principle of the dynamo and the electric motor. Faraday also found that electricity flowing in one coil of wire can produce a current flowing in another coil nearby; this is the theoretical basis for the transformer. The actual experiments in which these and other facts were discovered were performed in the amazingly short span of ten days.

The development of the electric motor progressed swiftly, and it was soon a practical source of power, although oddly enough the dynamo, entirely similar in principle, remained for years little more than a laboratory curiosity. To some extent this inequality was due to the use of the battery, in the invention of which one of the pioneers had been Alessandro Volta, a professor in the University of Pavia. The battery offered a ready-made source of electric power, and battery-driven motors were soon in experimental use. But this type of power was about sixty times as expensive as steam power, and it was clear that some other source of electrical energy was necessary to supplant the battery.

THE STATOR AND THE ROTOR

Electric motors are among the most common of modern sources of power supply. Like the generator they operate on the principle of interaction of electromagnetic fields of force. There are two essential parts of an electric motor, a stator, in which a magnetic field is produced, and a rotor armature through whose

A MAGNETIC MACHINE OF 1871

Paul's Photos. Chicago

ERNST WERNER SIEMENS, INVENTOR
OF THE DYNAMO

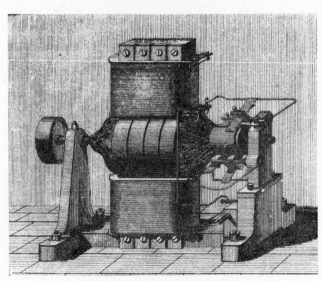

AN EARLY DYNAMO (1883)

coils another current passes which reacts against the magnetic field and causes a rotation, turning the axis of the armature. Industry and science have evolved endless varieties of motors, each adapted to the work it must do. Some utilize alternating current, some direct; the "universal" motor uses either, and there are many types and combinations of these varieties, such as the series, shunt, and compound wound direct-current motors and the one, two, three, and polyphase alternating-current types.

A NEW KIND OF HOOF IN THE HORSESHOE

The utilization of the electric generator at last brought the cost of electricity down to practical levels. Faraday's first dynamo, which he constructed in 1831, was a copper disc rotating between the ends of a horseshoe magnet; electricity was conducted from the device by means of two contacts on the flat end of the disc, one at the axis and the other at the rim. Another generator was made in the next year by Pixii in which the magnetic field, the horseshoe, was improved by the substitution of unlike poles, which produced greater magnetic force. The armature, Faraday's disc, was made more efficient by a coil of wire to guide the induction. The permanent magnets of these early dynamos were replaced by electromagnets in the experiments of Wheatstone, in 1845. Other experimenters in electromagnetics continued the improvement of the generator; among them were Gramme, von Siemens, Alteneck, Hopkinson, Weston, Steinmetz, and the ubiquitous Edison. The armature was made of laminated metal rather than a single solid piece, and the wiring of the armature was placed in slots; so that the distance between it and the field could be reduced. Development of the generators was rapid, and as their use spread they were constructed in great variety, ranging from tiny devices which can be held on the tip of one finger, to the huge, softly humming monsters capable of supplying power for whole cities. Variations in type were nearly as great as those in size. Horizontal shafts and vertical shafts, rotating armatures and revolving fields, direct-current and alternating-current production, all found a place in the expanding field of power generation. They were turned by steam turbines and by water power, by

LATE 19TH CENTURY WATER WHEEL GENERATOR

engines and by electric motors. Except for a few specialized sorts of work, such as electric railways, electrolytic methods, and the supplying of power to metropolitan districts, alternating current largely replaced direct. The stationary armature and revolving field supplanted, to a great extent, the armature which turned in its field and necessitated the use of brushes to convey the current from it.

THE "TEEMING BRAIN"

The world of electricity provided stimulation for many of the great minds in the vanguard of the advancing front of science. Many of these men turned their inventive minds to problem after problem in the world, finding brilliant solutions in the miracles of electricity. Edison is probably the best known of these pioneers, but there were many others. One of the most amazing

Courtesy General Electric Co.

NEVADA GENERATOR ROOM AT BOULDER DAM

Courtesy National Broadcasting Co.

HUGE GENERATOR IN SERVICE AT RADIO CITY

geniuses, Nikola Tesla, came to the United States from Croatia in 1884; in many ways he is typical of the modern electrical workers. Tesla's induction motor made the first effective use of alternating current; he made pioneering use of the rotary magnetic field and polyphase transmission in his design of the Niagara Falls hydroelectric plant. His work in wireless communication and power transmission to a great extent underlies modern broadcasting. He also experimented with incandescent lamps without filaments, photography by fluorescent and phosphorescent light, and invented new forms of induction coils, transformers, generators, and condensers.

THE SILENT MARCHING GIANTS

Engine-driven generators are used in automobiles to charge the storage battery; steam turbines turn the mighty dynamos in many great ocean liners. Perhaps the most dramatic electric generators are those of the great hydroelectric plants, such as those located at Niagara Falls; at the Norris Dam, in the Tennessee Valley; and at the gigantic Boulder Dam in the Colorado River. Electric power has many advantages over other forms of energy because of its transportability. The generator operates to produce power where the energy to run it is cheap, such as at the great waterfalls and dams. The electricity can then be transmitted more than 250 miles with negligible loss of power, through high-tension wires hung from tall poles, silent, marching giants which cross hill and valley, river and canyon. The generators ordinarily develop high currents at low voltage, and the voltage is then stepped up by transformers for more efficient transmission. Long-distance cables often carry as much as sixty thousand volts, a current which is stepped down at the places where it is used along the line. The development of these great hydroelectric plants and high-tension-line systems is steadily increasing the availability of cheap electric power.

Courtesy National Broadcasting Co.

MOTOR-GENERATOR SETS USED FOR PRODUCING CURRENT IN RADIO CITY

FAR, FAR back, before the dawn of history, our apelike ancestors made an important scientific discovery—fire. Fire set them apart from the other animals that roamed the earth. At first, fire was used for its warmth, later for cooking food; and finally our shaggy-browed forefathers discovered the wonder of artificial light. A fire before the cave lighted up the interior, frightened off wild animals, they found, and a bundle of dry twigs made a torch that could be carried about. Later on, small fires were sometimes built high up on the walls of the rude caves, just for illumination.

As civilization advanced, bowls of fats and oils, with grass wicks, were used for lighting. In the Mediterranean countries, olive oil was used; in America, whale oil. Over a period of years, lamps improved very slowly, even up to the nineteenth century, when gas lighting came into being. Gas light, terrifying as it seemed to the honest citizens at first, was a great improvement over the oil lamps, especially when the Welsbach mantle was produced. This was a small cone of cotton thread, dipped in a solution of rare earths. When placed in the gas flame, the cotton was slowly consumed, and the mantle glowed with a brilliant white light.

In 1801 Sir Humphrey Davy invented the electric arc light. This light consisted of a holder for two carbon rods, which were connected to an electric current. When the rods were separated a short distance, between them glowed a blue-white arc of carbon vapor, forming an intense, flickering, smoky glare.

THE INCANDESCENT LAMP

Thomas Alva Edison was the son of plain people of the Middle West. At eleven, he was conducting experiments in chemistry, and as his experiments grew more and more costly he looked for

EARLY TYPES OF INCANDESCENT LAMPS

ways of making money. At fifteen, he persuaded his parents to allow him to become a train newsboy. When he grew older, he became a telegraph operator, meanwhile spending every available moment in his laboratory. By 1877 he secured enough money to establish a laboratory in Menlo Park, New Jersey.

Young Edison's dream was an electric light for the home—for everyone's home. True, there was the arc lamp, but it was too large, required too much electric current, and was too troublesome. The arc burned too fiercely to be of practical use in a living room. Edison decided that the only solution of the problem was a lamp that burned in a vacuum, so that air would not be allowed to consume the material that was heated by the current. The young inventor intended to furnish lights that could be used anywhere, and he proposed to "pipe" electric power into homes,

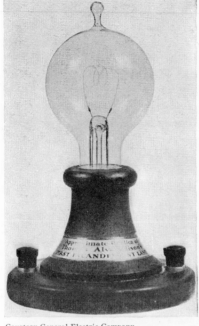

Courtesy General Electric Company
FIRST COMMERCIAL
INCANDESCENT LAMP
Edison's carbonized bamboo filament lamp
placed in service in 1878.

like gas. World-renowned scientists smiled at the ambitious young man, and agreed that it couldn't be done. Burning anything in a vacuum, where it would have no oxygen to consume, was abhorrent to all scientific knowledge. A famous English scientist said: "It's ridiculous —I'd rather have this Edison try it, than I."

Edison's first incandescent lamp consisted of a strip of charred paper, supported in a glass vessel from which the air had been exhausted by a hand pump. The ends of the strip were connected to a source of electricity. On the first trial, the frail strip of carbon glowed for eight minutes before burning up. Then came hundreds of trials using strips and threads of every imaginable substance. Edison even pulled hairs from beards and moustaches to experiment with. Finally, in 1879, after fourteen months and the expenditure of a great deal of money, a bulb with a filament of carbonized thread was built. Hopefully, Edison and his assistants watched as the current was applied. The lamp glowed, and the little group of scientists tensely watched. How long would it glow, before burning out? They watched, sleepless, for forty hours! This first incandescent bulb finally flickered out, and as the group started wearily toward their beds, Edison said: "I know I can make one burn a hundred hours." He did.

More than six thousand substances were tested in the ceaseless search for a long-burning lamp filament. One hot day, the inventor sat fanning himself with a bamboo fan. Suddenly he ripped a thread of bamboo from the frame. "Test this," he said to an assistant. The bamboo, charred, turned out to be the finest material yet found, and Edison sent men all over the world to find other tropical plants. This search took months, cost $100,-000, and proved that bamboo fiber was still the best material. Night and day the little factory in Menlo Park kept manufacturing the incandescent bulbs; people were clamoring for electric lights for their homes.

Quite independently an incandescent lamp was invented by Swan in England before Edison had invented his.

THE FIRST CENTRAL LIGHTING STATION

In 1882 the Pearl Street Station, the world's first Central Lighting Plant, was built in New York. Although the design

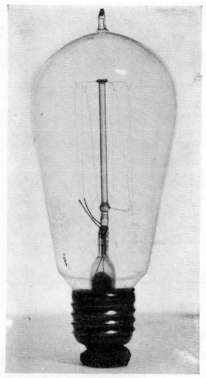

Courtesy General Electric Company

THE DRAWN WIRE TUNGSTEN FILAMENT LAMP OF 1907

seemed perfect on paper, the dynamos refused to behave properly. At first, short circuits and minor explosions were daily occurrences, and wide-eyed gossips ran around with tales of horses going wild in the streets, becoming tangled up in stray electric currents. These were the same timid horses which were frightened a few years before by the telephone, and some of the poor beasts might well be frightened, for a new type of "horse-power" was in the offing. However, horses or no horses, the plant was put in operation, and many New York homes began to glow with the wonderful new electric lights.

The first carbon-filament bulbs were not entirely satisfactory, and they gave way to wires made of a gun-cotton solution. A thick syrup of this material was squirted through fine holes in a

Courtesy General Electric Company

MODERN LIVING ROOM LIGHTING

Courtesy General Electric Company

MODERN TYPE LAMPS DEVELOPED IN 1924

Coiled drawn wire tungsten filament operating in an inert gas.

THE FLOODLIGHTED MERCHANDISE MART IN CHICAGO

platinum plate, and the new fine wire was then hardened in alcohol. Edison had thus copied the technique of the web-spinning spider. At this point he felt that his work with the incandescent bulb was finished, and he passed on to other important things, leaving further improvement to the General Electric Company.

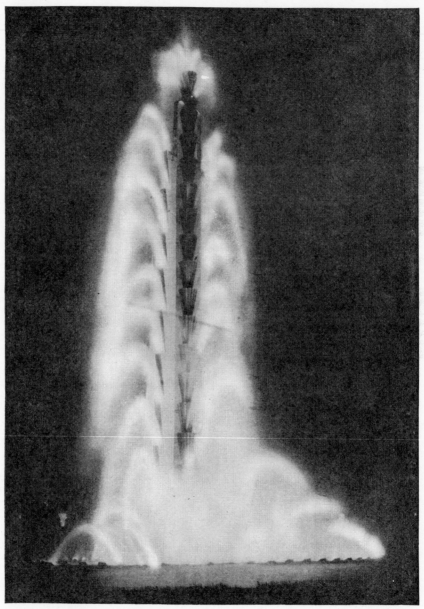

Paul's Photos, Chicago

MAGIC FOUNTAIN AT PARIS SHOWING THE WITCHERY OF
MODERN LIGHTING

Courtesy General Electric Company

DAYLIGHT DRIVING AT NIGHT ON AN ILLUMINATED HIGHWAY

From the laboratories of this company, and through the genius of men like Dr. Irving Langmuir, a constantly improved bulb has been forthcoming; the carbon bulb of thirty years ago has become a highly evacuated, gas-filled, tungsten bulb; large lights are now filled with nitrogen, and special lamps are made for different purposes. The simple device that burned only forty hours has grown into a huge family of useful light-giving devices, that perform such diverse feats as projecting motion pictures and furnishing an artificial sun-tan.

Recently the Edison Memorial was dedicated at Menlo Park, New Jersey, to the memory of the genius who gave us the electric light, the most radical improvement in lighting since the dim days of hand torches. This beautiful monument contains a huge electric bulb that took months to manufacture. Its power comes from several central stations, and despite any power-failure, the Edison Memorial will burn through the ages—a vivid, glowing tribute to the man who gave us light.

THE PHOTOELECTRIC cell, often called the "electric eye," is one of the most amazing, versatile, and useful inventions of recent years. This little device, so small that it can be carried in one's pocket, has already relieved mankind of hundreds of monotonous, disagreeable tasks. It does things that human beings cannot do—it sees in the dark and detects incredibly minute differences in color and intensity of light. The photoelectric cell is used in many branches of industry, in stores and offices, and even in private homes. Yet it is really an extremely simple piece of apparatus.

The predecessor of the modern photoelectric cell was the selenium cell. In 1873 an Englishman, Willoughby Smith, discovered quite by accident that the electrical resistance of the metal selenium was lowered when light fell upon it. This property makes it possible, for example, to hook up a selenium cell with a relay and motor so that light falling on the cell may start the motor, which may then do useful work. Many private garage doors open by this scheme when the owner's auto headlights shine on a cell attached to the door. (See diagram.) But the selenium

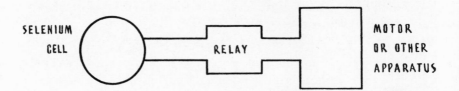

cell is lazy—it requires a second or more to get to work or to stop. For this reason it is seldom used at present, since other types of cells are better adapted to the various tasks in which an electric eye is needed.

The newer caesium cell works by a different principle from that of the selenium. Its principle was discovered by the grandfather of radio, Heinrich Hertz, while he was performing his famous experiments with the spark gap. He, however, was too busy with his electromagnetic wave experiments to pursue the subject, and it remained for the German physicist, Hallwachs, to investigate the effect of light on metals and announce it in 1888. Elster and Geitel soon found that the more chemically active a metal is, the more readily it will convert light into electricity. Some of these metals are sodium (which is in ordinary table salt), potassium, rubidium, and caesium.

At first this principle remained only a scientific curiosity. But scientific discovery is sooner or later put to work, no matter how useless it may seem when first encountered. That is the reason why large industrial companies maintain expensive research laboratories; the cost is more than repaid in the long run. It was so with the experiments of Hallwachs and Hertz—mankind in general has lately reaped the benefits of those purely scientific experiments of half a century ago.

The first actual photoelectric cell was devised by Stotelow in 1890, but could find almost no uses because the current of electricity it produced was so small. The modern cells give only a weak current, too, but vacuum-tube amplifiers are now used to increase the current to a useful value. The modern photocell is an evacuated tube which is coated on the inside with one of the above-mentioned metals, usually caesium. The tube is connected with a battery. When light falls on the metal coating a weak electric current flows through the tube; and the more intense the light, the stronger will be the current passing through. This kind of cell does not lag appreciably in changing light into electricity —it is not at all lazy.

THE CELL IN HOLLYWOOD

As soon as the ambitious young photoelectric cell grew up, it found plenty of work to do. It went to Hollywood, entered the moving picture industry, and made possible the talking pictures. Moving pictures that talked had long been the fanciful dream of

P & A Photo, N. Y.

WAVE OF GARY'S HAND STARTS NEW MILL OPERATING

This picture vividly portrays the wonders of modern electrical engineering. On the
occasion of the opening of the U. S. Steel Corporation's electrified Homestead
plant near Pittsburgh, Judge Elbert H. Gary, seated in his office in New York
City, passed his hand over a globe containing a light-sensitive cell.
Through telegraph and short-wave radio the impulse was sent to
Homestead, where it closed the switch setting the mills in operation.

inventors, especially of Thomas Edison. The only practical system before the photoelectric cell was to synchronize a phonograph
with the film. By employing the photocell it became possible to
turn sound into light, to reproduce the light in a track on the
film and with a photocell in the projector, to reconvert the light
into sound. Exactly this procedure is now employed to make compact sound records on film instead of using the bulky and break-
able wax phonograph records.

Some types of photoelectric cells are sensitive to light waves
of a kind which the human eye cannot see, just as some animals
can hear sounds which are pitched too high for human ears. These

cells are well suited for burglar alarms. Suppose we have a small lamp giving off a beam of ultra-violet light, popularly known as "black light," since its rays are invisible to the human eye. If this lamp were turned on in a dark room, its rays would still be dark to us—but not to the electric eye. Point the ultra-violet beam across a doorway so that it strikes a photoelectric cell connected to an alarm system. If someone comes through the doorway, interrupting the beam, the cell may start the alarm, switch on the electric lights, call the police, set off a tear-gas bomb, and generally make the intruder feel unwelcome.

Another uncanny use of this versatile instrument is in the inspection of materials. With absolute accuracy the photoelectric cell can separate materials of slightly different colors, shapes, or densities, and can detect rust spots or flaws in sheets of metal or glass.

On some highways at certain places two cells are set up a short distance apart. The time that an automobile takes to pass from one to the other is automatically recorded. Dr. Thomas, of the Westinghouse Company, has invented a method of traffic control for suburban districts, the brain of which is a photoelectric cell. Railway and subway signals are often operated by the electric eye.

The wonderful thing about the photoelectric cell is not the cell itself, for it is quite simple, but the many ingenious and clever ways in which it is harnessed to do man's tasks

EVER SINCE the discovery of electricity man has been interested in the possibility of sending messages over wires. If only this could be accomplished, the problem of communication would be immensely simplified. In the early nineteenth century it took weeks and weeks for the people of the American nation to learn of important events. In 1815, at the close of the war between England and the United States, a bloody battle was fought on American soil a few weeks after peace had been reached in England, simply because it was not known here that the American delegates in England had concluded a treaty.

Yet, for the sake of historical accuracy, it must be stated that, when the telegraph was invented, people were not very enthusiastic over it. They regarded the new invention more or less as a scientific toy. Only a dramatic occurrence, in both the United States and England, served to make the telegraph popular with the mass of people.

Charles Wheatstone, English physicist, was one of the first men to make a workable telegraph. When only fifteen years old,

EARLY SKETCH SHOWING THE OPERATION OF THE FIRST TELEGRAPH

amidst great hardships and poverty, he began to experiment with electricity. Later he became interested in problems of acoustics and sound. He was so shy that he did not dare read his scientific reports in public, and on more than one occasion the famous Faraday had to read Wheatstone's papers before the Royal Society. In 1834, however, Wheatstone was appointed Professor of Experimental Philosophy in King's College, London University.

Because electric current traveled so rapidly, Wheatstone conceived the possibility of utilizing it for the sending of messages. Together with William F. Cooke, he worked incessantly in his laboratories. Their labors were richly rewarded, for in 1837 these two men invented the first practical telegraph.

Their new invention was at first quite simple in construction. At the receiving end of the line a magnetic needle, suspended in a coil of wire, would turn left or right automatically whenever the current was switched to a different direction. The man who operated the receiver could read the message easily, since the needle pointed to letters arranged on a dial. This type of telegraph was used in England until the superior Morse telegraph came into general use.

At first, the general public in England showed little interest, as is often the case with new inventions. A dramatic episode took place, however, which suddenly changed this lethargic attitude. In one of the suburbs of London a murder took place, and the suspect had been seen taking the train to London. Ordinarily this would have been equivalent to escape, since no faster method of transportation or communication than the train then existed. Now, suddenly, someone thought of the telegraph, and a description of the criminal was at once sent to London by wire. Upon his arrival he was promptly arrested and eventually convicted. Great publicity was given to this feat, and at once the telegraph became popular with the English public, who now realized its immense value.

Almost simultaneously with Wheatstone, someone in the United States was working independently on the telegraph. Later he was to be known as one of the great men of history. His name was Samuel Finley Breese Morse.

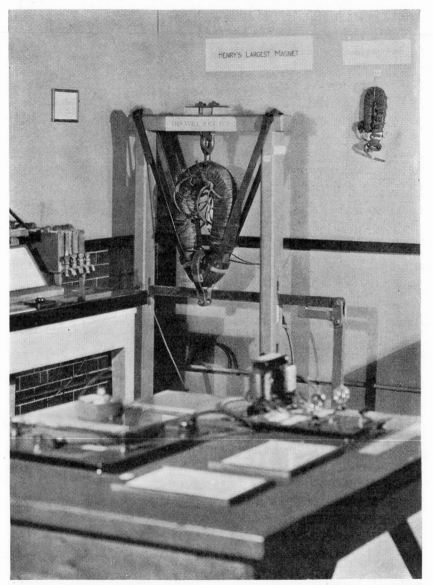

Courtesy Museum of Science and Industry, Chicago

MODEL OF JOSEPH HENRY'S MAGNETO
Henry was one of the early experimenters with the electric telegraph.

Courtesy Western Union Telegraph Co.

MORSE TRANSMITS ORIGINAL TELEGRAM

This contemporary woodcut shows the inventor tapping out his first message, "What hath God wrought," over the line he had constructed from Washington to Baltimore.

FROM PAINTING TO TELEGRAPH

Strangely enough, the early career of Morse did not give the slightest indication that some day he was to be famous for a scientific invention. He was born in 1791 at Charlestown, Massachusetts, the son of a Congregational minister. Early in life he became interested in painting and art, and when a mere youth he painted beautiful water colors. While at Yale university he painted the "Landing of the Pilgrims," and upon graduation set out for England to study art. He was quite successful and when he returned to the United States three years later, he was acclaimed as a great artist by the people of Boston. For some time he succeeded in making a meager living from his paintings, and in 1826 he was elected President of the National Academy of Arts and Design and lectured on fine arts. It was in 1832, while returning from a journey to Europe, that Morse conceived the idea of the modern telegraph.

Courtesy Western Union Telegraph Co.

THE SIMPLEX PRINTER—A TELETYPE-WRITER

On a stormy night, in mid-ocean, a group of gentlemen were engaged in a serious discussion of electricity in the cabin of the sail ship, *Sully*. They all knew of the accomplishments of Benjamin Franklin, who had sent an electric current through seven miles of wire. One of the passengers, Dr. Charles T. Jackson, explained to his eager listeners the experiments of Ampère which he had witnessed in Paris. He also demonstrated a small electromagnet which he had in his possession.

Of all those present, Morse was fascinated the most by the subject under discussion. Although he knew nothing about the work on the telegraph by previous inventors, his fertile imaginative mind then and there conceived the plan for a device to send and receive messages by means of electricity. Enthusiastically he told those present about his plan. "Why, gentlemen," he declared, "I tell you, it means a revolution in the world. If I can drive an electrical impulse through a length of copper wire and send it far enough, I'll girdle the world like 'Puck.' I'll talk with the Khan of Tartary as easily as I talk with you."

That night Morse excitedly paced the deck of the rolling ship, then in his cabin he made a drawing of the incipient invention. Landing in New York harbor, he shook hands with the captain and said: "Should you hear of the Telegraph one of these days as the wonder of the world, remember that the discovery was made on the good ship *Sully*."

Yet, for many years Morse was not able to perfect his device. Continually, he was troubled by financial difficulties and had not enough funds to carry on his experiments. Materials to work with were scarce in those days and he had to make his own batteries and electromagnets.

After the first set was made he appeared to be faced by certain defeat. The current running through the wire was not strong enough to operate the arm connected with the magnet. It seemed that the instrument was useless in practice.

THE MORSE CODE IS BORN

In 1835 Morse received an appointment to the University of New York because of his reputation in art. While teaching art, he continued to experiment. He came in contact with Professor Joseph Henry, who was noted for his work in electromagnetism. The latter helped Morse a great deal in overcoming his difficulties. By wrapping many turns of fine wire around a piece of soft iron, Henry had devised an extremely sensitive electromagnet. Using this type of electromagnet, Morse was able to progress with his work and constructed a crude telegraph. The current was short-circuited and thus the armature of the magnet moved, making dots and dashes on a paper tape turned by clockwork. The dots and dashes, in various combinations, stood for the letters of the alphabet, and later were known as the Morse code.

Thus Morse was able to send messages over a wire if the latter was not too long. But whenever the wire was of great length, the resistance weakened the current to such an extent that it was

Courtesy Western Union Telegraph Co.

SIMPLEX PRINTER WITH COVER REMOVED

unable to move the armature of the magnet. Finally, Morse also overcame this difficulty by inventing the now famous "relay"— an electrical device which picked up the alternating current and reinforced it. The modern telegraph was now completed! Messages could be sent along wires around the entire world and soon a network of wires crossed and recrossed the continents.

Morse now needed capital in order to make his invention a commercial success and to bring it into general use. Fortunately, Morse met Alfred Vail, who became so interested in the project that he persuaded his father to invest several thousand dollars in it. The telegraph was patented in the year 1837 and Congress after much debate appropriated thirty thousand dollars to build an experimental telegraph line between Baltimore and Washington. When the attempt to place the wires under ground failed they were strung on poles, and on May 24, 1844, Morse sitting in the Capitol in Washington, sent to Vail in Baltimore the historic message, "What hath God wrought," and Vail immediately telegraphed back the identical words.

The United States government, however, refused to buy Morse's invention. Private corporations which paid Morse great sums for his patents were thereupon organized. Thus Morse, shortly before his death in 1872, became extremely wealthy, and in addition was honored with decorations and medals from the important nations of the world.

Later, many refinements and developments of the telegraph came into general use. Thomas A. Edison, a telegraph operator in his youth, made improvements in the Morse telegraph. By studying the telegraph instruments and stock tickers he was able to devise a method of sending four messages over the same line at one time.

Dr. H. A. Rowland of Johns Hopkins University invented the printing telegraph which could send eight messages over a wire at one time. He used a keyboard similar to that of the typewriter and when a key was struck the corresponding key on the receiving end did not reproduce a dot or dash but the actual letter of the alphabet. Modern telegraphy has been reduced to the simple operation of typing the message at the sending station and having it automatically reproduced at the receiving end on an automatic electric typewriter.

ATLANTIC CABLE

The laying of the Atlantic cable is one of the most fascinating chapters in the story of the telegraph. Under immense difficulties and after years of hard labor this herculean task was finally accomplished. The name of the great pioneer, Cyrus W. Field, will forever be connected with this achievement.

In 1857, the first attempt was made with 2,500 miles of cable consisting of seven copper wires, well insulated. Two warships, one from the United States, the other from England, started out with the cable, planning to meet each other in mid-ocean, where the cable ends were to be spliced. Unfortunately, when the *Niagara*, the American ship, had proceeded four hundred miles, the cable broke and the ships had to return. The following year a similar failure took place.

Though large sums had been lost, Field again organized the venture, and the next year the attempt was successful. President Buchanan and Queen Victoria congratulated each other by telegraph. But after a month had passed the insulation of the wires burned because of too high voltages, and once more America and Europe were left without telegraphic communication. Not till

Associated Press photo

WIREPHOTO SENDING SET

1866 did Field succeed in establishing permanent connections. Since then the Atlantic Ocean, and all the other seas and oceans of the world, have been spanned by numerous telegraph cables, which now encircle the entire globe.

PHOTOS BY WIRE

The development of the art of sending photographs by wire is one which is marked by the contributions of many individuals and by many research laboratories. The company which made it a practical commercial reality, in the United States at least, was the Radio Corporation of America. The method or methods of sending a photograph by wire depends upon the action of a photoelectric cell. At the sending end of the apparatus a black and white photograph is wrapped around a cylinder and a tiny beam of light is focussed upon it and the reflections of this light are in turn transmitted to a photoelectric cell.

As the cylinder revolves, it brings light and dark areas into the beam of light, and the whiter areas cause a greater stream of electrons to leave the cell. Dark areas cause few or no electrons to leave. These electrons are amplified and sent either over wires or by radio to the receiving station as electrical impulses. The intensity of these impulses depends upon the amount of white, gray, or black area in the original photograph.

At the receiving station these impulses are again transformed by a photoelectric cell and are focussed on a sensitized film rotating in synchronization with the sending cylinder. These waves "paint" a fine line of varying intensity on the film and when it is developed these appear as a print of the original. The earlier type of receiving set used the incoming impulses to operate an air brush which inked the photograph on a moving strip of paper.

OUR EARLIEST ancestors first had to learn to talk, in order to communicate their thoughts to one another. As time went on, men learned to write, and communication over long distances became possible, far beyond the sound of their voices. However, this was a slow way of carrying information, for letters took time to write, and the rapidity of transit was limited by the speed of locomotion. In 1844 the telegraph came into use. This was a great improvement in communication, but only trained operators could use the apparatus, and turn words into dots and dashes and back again. Men still dreamed of actually sending their voices over long distances.

THE FIRST TELEPHONE

In 1872 a young Scotchman named Alexander Graham Bell came to Boston from Canada, to accept a position in a school for deaf mutes. He was an expert in phonetics, the science of sounds, but his school work took up most of his time, although he was working on a model for a new telegraph instrument. Soon, however, he opened a school of his own, and it was possible for him to spend more time on the harmonic telegraph, as it was called. This device was designed to allow the simultaneous transmission of many different messages over one telegraph wire. Each message was to be sent by a vibrator that sent out a certain musical note, or frequency, and at the other end of the line a corresponding vibrator was to respond to only one certain note. Each sender and receiver was much like the door buzzers we use today. If this device could be made to work, many messages could be sent at the same time, as each receiver would respond to only a certain note, and each sender would be tuned differently.

One day Bell and his assistant, Thomas A. Watson, were experimenting with their harmonic telegraph, when a contact on one of the senders stuck. Attempting to loosen it, Watson plucked

ALEXANDER
GRAHAM BELL,
INVENTOR OF
THE TELEPHONE
Courtesy Illinois Bell
Telephone Co.

the vibrator with his finger. Suddenly Bell dashed in from the
next room, where the receivers were located. The receiver had
sounded a musical note, just as the sender did when Watson
plucked it with his fingers. A musical sound had been sent over a
wire. The telephone was born. That same day Bell made plans
for a new model, and Watson, the mechanic, excitedly went to
work.

Although progress was rapid, it was forty weeks before speech
could actually be heard over the telephone. The vibrating reed,
corresponding to the clapper of our door-buzzer, had been replaced with a diaphragm of gold-beaters' skin, with a mouthpiece
in front. One day Bell shouted into his instrument, "Please come
here, Mr. Watson, I want you!" There was a crash in the other
room as Watson dropped his instrument to the floor and dashed

BELL'S BOX TELEPHONE
First telephone put into commercial
use in 1877.

MAGNETO BELL SUBSCRIBER SET
The range of transmission was extended
by the use of a more powerful
battery transmitter.

in, crying, "I heard you!" This speech, although not nearly so
dramatic, was to go down in history with that of Morse, the inventor of the telegraph, when he tapped out, "What hath God
wrought."

The Philadelphia Centennial Exposition was about to open,

and it seemed an ideal stage on which to present to the world this newest invention. The original model, placed on display, was a simple device, similar to the telephone receiver of today. It consisted of a permanent bar magnet, surrounded by a coil of wire, with a soft iron disk placed on the end. The same device was used for both talking and listening.

Only a small, out of the way table was obtained at the exhibition, and no one seemed much interested in Bell's "toy." The tired judges of the exhibition, just finishing their inspection, were about to pass the table by, when suddenly one of their number rushed up to the disheartened inventor. It was an old friend, Dom Pedro, emperor of Brazil. The emperor greeted his old friend warmly, and placed his ear to the receiver. Suddenly he shrieked: "My God, it talks!" Fortunately this telephone was a table model, and it wasn't sent crashing to the floor. The judges crowded around to hear the new marvel; overnight, Bell became famous.

As the telephone became popular, different individuals claimed credit for the invention, and Bell and his newly formed company fought the first of six hundred successful battles in the courts. His greatest victory was that over the Western Union Telegraph Company which finally surrendered their monopoly of the telephone field. They had a superior transmitter, invented by Edison, but soon afterward the Bell Company developed a carbon transmitter, similar to the one in use today. Previously, transmitter and receiver were identical. This microphone consisted of a diaphragm linked with a small cup of carbon granules. When sound reached the diaphragm, it moved back and forth, compressing and releasing the bits of carbon, in sympathy with the words spoken into the mouthpiece. The action on the granules varied the resistance of the device, and the resulting pulsating electric current caused a receiver to repeat the words spoken into the transmitter.

THE TELEPHONE EXCHANGE

A telephone exchange is a central station with which all telephones are connected. When one person wishes to talk to another, he calls the exchange, where an operator connects his telephone line to that of the person with whom he wishes to speak. This

Courtesy Illinois Bell Telephone Co

SWITCHBOARD IN A DIAL CENTRAL OFFICE

makes it unnecessary to run wires from each telephone to every other telephone. The first telephone exchange was built in Boston in 1877. The early operators of this converted telegraph switchboard were boys, who scrambled about tangled up in their wires, and frequently insulted the subscribers. They were soon replaced with young ladies who were taught to say "Number, please" politely, and to apologize prettily for all wrong numbers. Wrong numbers were not at all uncommon, either: most of the telephone jokes we hear today have come down to us from the early days of the telephone. One man, in fact, became so very indignant at wrong numbers and busy signals that he accused his business competitors of underhand dealings with the telephone company. This Kansas City undertaker, Almon B. Strowger, on one occasion became so provoked that he sat up all night building a model of a device that would make connections automatically, and dispense with the operator. This device grew into the automatic switchboard, a complicated device of selective circuits, and the dial telephone came into being.

In modern telephone systems, it is unnecessary to ask the operator for a local connection. One merely twirls a dial on his own telephone, and machinery does the rest. Although fewer operators are required, this marvelous device has not thrown people out of work, because the complicated automatic circuits require a large, highly skilled crew for maintenance, not to mention the thousands who build and service telephone equipment.

THE LONG-DISTANCE TELEPHONE

When people began to realize what a boon to mankind the telephone was destined to be, the telephone system spread over the country practically overnight. In 1892 a telephone line was put into operation between New York and Chicago. As telephone engineers attempted to string their wires over hundreds of miles, new difficulties arose, for it was necessary to strengthen the feeble telephone currents, so they would travel over long reaches of wire. For this purpose repeaters or amplifiers, invented by Dr. Michael Pupin and called loading coils, were used, and placed at intervals along the lines. When De Forest invented his vacuum tube, it was immediately applied in telephony.

Another disadvantage of the rapidly growing popularity of the telephone was the web of overhead wires that soon made a network over the streets of the large cities, snaring the kites of the little boys, and, more seriously, collecting ice and snow and falling to the ground. Underground cables were the next development. These lead-sheathed cables contain hundreds of pairs of wires, insulated from each other by paper wrappings. They are connected together in manholes in the streets, and terminate in huge vaults in the basements of the telephone exchanges, where the thousands of wires are separated into pairs and connected with their proper places.

In 1915 the first transcontinental telephone line was put into operation. On the first day, Mr. Bell, in Boston, telephoned to Mr. Watson in San Francisco: "Please come here, Mr. Watson, I want you"—and Mr. Watson laughingly replied: "It would take me a week, now." Mr. Watson didn't drop the telephone in amazement, *this* time. By 1927, when Lindbergh flew the Atlantic, a transatlantic telephone, utilizing radio communication to span the ocean, connected London with New York, and two years later it was possible to sit at any telephone in the United States and talk to a dozen of the largest ocean liners on the Atlantic.

The telephone has become firmly intrenched among the other necessities of life. Our home telephone can be connected to more than ninety per cent of all the telephones in the world. The large, unsightly wall telephone has given way to a single-unit cradle type instrument that contains its own bell box; in some cities the telephone directory is larger than the telephone instrument itself.

Alexander Graham Bell never did succeed in inventing the harmonic telegraph, but his telephone has brought the most remote corners of the world just as near as the shiny black device on our telephone stand.

Courtesy Illinois Bell Telephone Co.

NEW TYPE TELEPHONE WITH
ENCLOSED BELL

T HE FIRST MEN who appeared on the earth were not greatly different from the large apes. Later on, as this strange animal developed, he learned how to make crude weapons; he discovered the wonder of fire, and in other ways he started the long, long journey toward civilization. One of his first steps toward superiority over the beasts was his power of speech. Most animals are able more or less to converse among themselves, but early man rapidly developed a vocabulary—and he probably liked to talk then as much as he does now. As centuries rolled on, man learned to communicate over long distances by writing letters. Finally came the telegraph, the cable and the telephone—but a time was coming when men would be able to talk to other men at the ends of the earth, without even stringing telephone wires.

Early in the nineteenth century, Michael Faraday, a keenly intelligent self-educated young Englishman, began to study a queer phenomenon called "induction." Without formal education of any kind, he began experiments with that mysterious something known as electricity: one day he discovered that an electric current appeared in a coil of wire if a magnet was thrust through its center. Then came another startling discovery: a moving wire, carrying an electricity current, if brought near another wire, would cause an electric current to be set up in the unattached conductor. Faraday found it impossible to explain this strange power—he called it "action at a distance."

James Clerk Maxwell, a famous mathematician, furnished an explanation of Faraday's mysterious "action at a distance." Maxwell showed mathematically that light waves and Faraday's electromagnetic waves were of similar form. Both traveled at the astounding speed of 186,000 miles per second, he said, and electromagnetic waves could be reflected and refracted, just like light waves. The only difference between them, he showed, was their length, or wave-length: Faraday's waves were too long to see.

Courtesy National Broadcasting Co.

A BATTERY OF HUGE TUBES USED IN BROADCASTING

MARCONI HONORS VOLTA
The inventor of wireless shown at ceremonies commemorating the 100th
anniversary of the birth of the scientist and inventor, Alessandro Volta.

When Maxwell published his startling theory, numerous scientists attempted to make these waves visible, so they might be studied. Finally Heinrich Hertz, a German university professor, succeeded. Dr. Hertz generated flashes of electricity in his laboratory, and detected them across the room with what he called a "resonator." This device was merely a slit metal ring, two edges of which were separated a small distance. When electromagnetic waves were sent out by the sender, the resonator showed a train of sparks across the opening. Although this experiment proved only part of Maxwell's theory, scientists over the entire world began to study these remarkable "Hertzian Waves."

WIRELESS EMERGES

During the next fourteen years, little was accomplished with the Hertzian wave; of course, Sir William Crooks, a British man

Courtesy National Broadcasting Co.

TWIN MICROPHONES USED IN RADIO STUDIOS

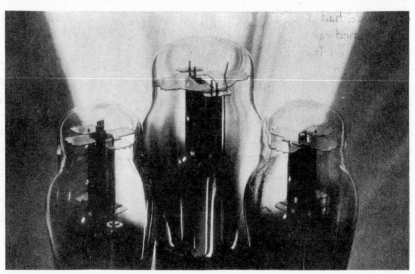

Courtesy National Broadcasting Co.

ELECTRON TUBES, HEART OF RADIO

Courtesy National Broadcasting Co.

A BANK OF LOUD SPEAKERS IN A THEATER

of science, had prophesied wireless telegraphy, but only one young man seemed earnestly at work on such a device. He was a twenty-two-year-old Italo-Irishman named Guglielmo Marconi. In London, in 1897, using apparatus that had been built by others, Marconi succeeded in sending and receiving signals at a distance of four miles. Then came his first contribution to the new art: in place of a condenser in the transmitting apparatus, he substituted the capacity between an aerial wire and a ground connection.

When Marconi added the antenna and ground connection, improved radiation of his signals doubled their range. It is interesting to note that a directional antenna was used. Directional antennae, just now coming into general use, were first employed by Marconi at the dawn of radio.

Sir Oliver Lodge furnished the next improvement. He created "tuning" by proposing that both transmitter and receiver be adjusted to send and receive certain frequencies, or wave lengths.

Courtesy National Broadcasting Co.
BEHIND THE SCENES IN RADIO CITY
Maze of wiring in a broadcasting studio.

Marconi had run into difficulty when more than one sending station was on the air at the same time, as receivers accepted all signals indiscriminately. Radio was progressing, slowly.

In 1898, after signals were sent over the English Channel, the public began to realize that wireless telegraphy was a fact. Immediately, several ship owners requested installation of apparatus, and wireless began its heroic work in marine disasters—in 1912 it was destined to save the lives of 700 passengers in the *Titanic* disaster.

The English Channel conquered, Marconi and his little band of assistants looked for new fields to conquer—and they were invited to span the Atlantic! When this task was started, it seemed that all the powers of nature conspired to keep the Marconi Company from erecting their apparatus. However, despite wind, snow, rain, and sleet, the stations were completed in 1901; this same year the letter "s" was flashed from England to Newfoundland.

After signals had been sent across the ocean, it was necessary to improve the apparatus so that reliable communication could be maintained. Marconi's next invention was the magnetic detector, designed to "hear" signals. This device turned the radio waves into musical notes, broken into dots and dashes, that might be translated by ear, just as telegraph operators translated the clicking of their instruments.

Professor J. Ambrose Fleming, assistant to Marconi, was the first to understand that a radio detector was merely a rectifier; in other words, he realized that it was not some mysterious power that changed the Hertzian waves back into dots and dashes: the detector merely changed the rapidly alternating current into direct current, which had an effect on the telephone receivers.

Twenty-one years before, Edison had sealed a metal plate inside one of his incandescent bulbs, and then connected one terminal of a battery to this plate, and the other to one of the lamp filament connections. When the positive connection was placed in contact with the plate, a current flowed from the battery through the gas in the bulb to the plate, and back to the battery again. This was known as the "Edison Effect."

Professor Fleming started work on a rectifying device, utilizing the "Edison Effect." In 1904 his first "Fleming Valve" was completed: current passed only from the plate of his "valve" to the filament, and not from the filament to the plate. Although this new device worked, it gave no better results than the simple detectors then in use, but it was the forerunner of the instrument that was to be the life's blood of all radio apparatus in the future —the vacuum tube.

THE CRYSTAL DETECTOR

The crystal detector was discovered in 1906. This was the cheap, efficient detector familiar to every one who has built a simple radio set. It consisted of a mineral crystal held in a cup that formed one connection to the circuit; the other connection was made to a fine wire "cat's whisker" that gently contacted the crystal. When a sensitive spot was found on the crystal, it acted as a one-way valve in the set, changing the alternating radio

Courtesy Columbia Broadcasting System

MASTER CONTROL POINT OF INAUGURAL HOOK-UP
Coverage of the Roosevelt inauguration in 1937 was directed from this station located
under the platform in front of the Capitol. From here instructions
went out to various commentators placed at strategic points.

current into direct current which furnished the signals that were heard in the headphones. Today we credit the crystal set with a range of fifteen to twenty miles, but back at the start of the twentieth century this form of receiver was the most efficient in existence: when powerful signals were heard thousands of miles, they were heard on the crystal set. Operators were trained to hear the faintest sounds in the headphone—and most signals were very, very faint!

The radio transmitter of this period utilized the Poulson arc, a huge electric arc, somewhat similar to those once used for street lighting. The latter consisted of two carbon sticks that formed a brilliant white hot arc when a current was applied across them: the Poulson arc contained complicated arrangement of magnets, to strengthen the arc, and to keep it from blowing out. Unlike the simple arc, it burned not in air, but in a hydrocarbon atmosphere, formed by a reservoir that slowly fed grain alcohol into the arc chamber. Installations of this type, shortly after the World War, were replaced by vacuum tubes.

In the same year that the crystal detector was invented, a new type of transmitter was constructed by Professor Fessenden, an American. Arc transmitters emanated what was known as a "damped" wave; Fessenden's sender produced a continuous-wave, more readily detected, and more easily read. This complicated sending station relied on the use of a huge alternating current generator, revolving at tremendous speed, and furnishing current that reversed itself 100,000 times every second. With this new device, Professor Fessenden succeeded in sending music and speech over the air; up to then, all radio signals were in code, or dots and dashes.

By the use of a telephone microphone, Fessenden impressed on the radio wave the voice wave from the microphone, and on Christmas night, 1906, he sent out the first radio program in history. This first offering consisted of a vocal selection, a violin solo, the reading of verse, and then an invitation for all listeners to write in—the first request for "fan mail." Imagine the astonishment of ship's operators when they heard voices and music coming in, instead of dots and dashes!

THE THREE-ELEMENT VACUUM TUBE

Nineteen hundred and six was a great year of radio development; in this same year Dr. Lee de Forest, a radio engineer, added a third element, called a grid, to the Fleming valve. This modification made the vacuum tube vastly superior to the crystal. The vacuum tube could also be used as an amplifier, for magnifying the signal, and two or three could be coupled together to amplify a radio signal millions of times. The Grid acted as a trigger, controlling the electron flow in the tube, and made it infinitely more powerful and sensitive than the two-element Fleming valve. Immediately, the telephone company employed the new invention as repeaters on long-distance lines. With the invention of de Forest's "triode," radio made perhaps the largest stride in its development. Almost overnight radio "grew up."

In 1912, E. H. Armstrong developed "feed back"—the regenerative circuit. This made possible a cheap, powerful radio set,

Courtesy Columbia Broadcasting System

PORTABLE BROADCASTING STATION
This automobile housed one of several shortwave and high frequency broadcast
stations used during presidential inauguration broadcasts.

built with a minimum of parts, and possessing great sensitivity.
Regenerative receivers were the earliest broadcast sets. They
brought in stations loud and clear, it is true, but they also contributed terrific squealings and caterwaulings—when a "three-
circuit" was tuned to its most sensitive point, it sounded like the
collected wailings of a thousand banshees. It was an impartial
type of radio, too—not only did it howl into its own headphones
or loud speaker, but it wailed into the speakers of all other sets in
the neighborhood: actually, it was a low-powered continuous
wave transmitter.

RADIO IN WAR TIME

The World War hastened progress in radio development, as it
did in the aircraft field. Wireless communication was a necessity
to all governments, and each country did all in its power to hasten

advances in the new art. Armstrong, commissioned a major in the
Signal Corps of the U. S. Army, improved on Fessenden's original
heterodyne receiver, and finally developed the powerful super-
heterodyne set. It is still the finest radio circuit: today, all except
the very smallest of radios are super-heterodynes.

Arc and high frequency alternator transmitters have been
replaced with vacuum tube transmitters, as the versatile vacuum
tube makes an efficient oscillator, or high frequency generator.
Today, all sending stations are of this type, with the exception of
a few old-fashioned installations on certain freight-carrying ships.
The modern transmitter is much like the regenerative receiver in
principle. The latter, when in a regenerative state, sends out a
whistle over the air. The sending stations use large tubes and
higher voltages, and when their whistle is broadcast, it is broken up
into dots and dashes of the Morse code, or, in the case of a broadcasting station, "modulated" with the radio program.

Courtesy Columbia Broadcasting System
AN ACTUAL BROADCASTING SCENE
"March of Time" broadcast from Columbia studios, with "sound effects" man
in left foreground. Audiences are not admitted here.

Broadcast stations came into the radio picture in 1920. The first broadcasting license was issued in 1921, and within a few years there were hundreds of stations all over the country. The public clamored for radio parts and sets. These earliest broadcasters had practically free use of the air; they went on and off whenever they chose, and they sent out their signals on practically any wave length. You might have, for example, received a certain station at number sixty on your dial one day, and at number ten the next day. Even during a broadcasting period, the frequency sometimes shifted. The government came to the rescue of a harassed radio public, however, and the Radio Commission was created in 1927 to regulate the use of the air.

While public interest was focused on broadcasting, progress in short wave radio continued, aided considerably by the work of amateur radio operators. In 1927 beam-transmission was first used commercially; soon the transatlantic radio telephone was put in operation. For this service, huge sending and receiving units were erected on carefully chosen spots on the Atlantic Coast. In these complicated installations, each receiver is large enough to

Courtesy Columbia Broadcasting System

"MARCH OF TIME" CONTROL ROOM
Here the engineers, completely insulated from actual studio sounds, listen to the program as it sounds on the air.

RADIO SPEEDS AID IN EMERGENCIES

Radio dramatically proved its worth in the great Ohio-Mississippi flood of 1936, when it was often the only quick means of directing relief and policing operations.

fill completely a small room. The entire plant covers many acres, and far beyond the buildings extend long antenna networks.

The amazing growth of commercial aviation is due in a large measure to radio. Directional beams keep air-liners on their courses, and constant radio communication from ground stations have done much to make this newest form of transportation safe for everyone.

Radio has come a long way since that first crude experiment in the laboratory of Professor Hertz. Even the cheapest of modern radio sets are capable of receiving foreign stations. Complicated circuits have been designed to allow push-button selection of stations, and automatic control of volume and frequency. The sets of fifteen years ago sounded no better than the ordinary telephone; modern high-fidelity equipment has made possible faithful transmission and reproduction over the entire range of the musical scale.

Our modern radios seem such perfect instruments that we may find ourselves asking "what's next?" There is a new group of engineers on the job now. They are serious young men, just like those who first gave us radio; and these young men promise us—television!

THROUGH THE MEDIUM of radio man began to learn the art of disembodying the human personality, of taking his ears in a split of a moment to any point on the globe and reassembling them to listen to a political oration or a symphony orchestra. It was but a logical step for him then to long for the day when he could see, as well as hear, around the globe. In its strictest sense television is the seeing of distant objects electrically.

Who invented television? Here again we are faced with a question that cannot be answered with a single name. If we consider the first practical television device we find in it the scanning disc, an invention of a German scientist, Paul Nipkow, in 1884; the photoelectric cell the properties of which were first noted by Heinrich Hertz; the transmission principles of radio which Marconi perfected; the optical, chemical and mechanical devices of many others. If we consider the modern television transmitter and receiver we find that the cathode ray tube, developed by Dr. Alexander Zworykin in the United States, is another important addition. John L. Baird in England, Mihaly in Hungary, Ives and Jenkins and the laboratories of the Bell Telephone Company, General Electric, and the Westinghouse Electric and Manufacturing Company—all of these and many others have contributed to this new field.

Basically, television consists of moving a rapid mosaic of light over the object to be televised through the medium of a scanning disc with spirally arranged holes or with the more efficient cathode ray tube. This light mosaic is then translated into an electrical mosaic and broadcast as electromagnetic waves just as in radio. On the receiving end the procedure is reversed and the retranslation gives the image of the object.

TELEVISION IS ALREADY "ON THE AIR"

The sending and receiving of television images is much more easily accomplished over wires than through ether. Remarkable

Courtesy Philco Radio & Television Corporation

ABOVE: PREPARING FOR A
TELEVISION FASHION SHOW

RIGHT: PHILCO CAMERA TUBE
A television engineer about to place the
"electric eye" in the television camera.

THE PHILCO TELEVISION CAMERA

success has lately been achieved in sending televised scenes from New York to Philadelphia over the newly developed coaxial cable.

Although television programs have been "on the air" since 1926, the public has not responded to them with anything like the enthusiasm with which it greeted radio. This is not due to any unfamiliarity with the principles of television. Even in the early days of radio, before the crystal detector sets had become obsolete, the American family talked intelligently of such innovations as wave lengths, antennae, electromagnetism, microphones, etc.— words which were not only technical but were new to the layman's vocabulary. The chief reason why television has not as yet become a household word is the fact that inventors are unable to attain simplicity in design and clarity in transmission. The scanning disc has now become obsolete, and it is safe to predict that the improvements being made in the vast field of electronics will soon make good television apparatus at a reasonable price. No longer does the televised image flicker because of the slowess of each spot of light in tracing a complete image.

THOUSANDS OF YEARS AGO, man learned to write, and he began to collect the words of great men and women into books which would transmit their thinking from one generation to the next, so that human knowledge might go forward. The next great advance in communication was the invention of the printing press, which made books and periodicals available to everyone and which was responsible for the tremendous increase in popular education.

But, although the written word was preserved and spread, the spoken word was lost to future generations. The great orations of a Daniel Webster, the exquisite voice of a Jenny Lind, the sweet, smooth tones flowing from the violins of the great Guarnerius and Stradivarius, could be heard by only a few people.

Although attempts to reproduce sound had been made earlier, the great American inventor who finally invented the highly original mechanism which was to preserve and immortalize the human voice was Thomas Edison. While working for the railroad as a telegraph operator, he discovered that the telegraph could be greatly improved. In 1877 he began to work on the device, later known as the telegraph repeater, which greatly speeded up the reception of messages.

The repeater in many respects resembled the later disc-phonograph. An electromagnet equipped with a needle pressed dots and dashes onto a paper placed on top of a rotating disc. One day Edison heard musical sounds emanating from the disk, and that moment marked the conception of his phonograph. In his daybook he made the following notation: "Just tried experiment with diaphragm having an embossing point and held against paraffin paper moving rapidly. The speaking vibrations are in-

EARLY EDISON
PHONOGRAPH

dented nicely and there's no doubt that I shall be able to store up and reproduce automatically at any future time the human voice perfectly."

Despite the fact that he was working on many other inventions, Edison immediately set to work to develop this new product of his imagination. On August 12, 1877, he sketched a drawing and asked his trusted mechanic and aid, Kreusi, to execute the project. Although incredulous as to the final outcome, the latter faithfully followed Edison's instructions. The first phonograph ever constructed consisted of a thin iron diaphragm, sensitive to sound waves, a sharp metallic needle attached to the diaphragm, and a cylinder covered with tin foil. The latter received the markings and indentations of the needle, which vibrated as a result of the sound waves beating on the diaphragm.

THE FIRST RECORD

The machine was tried out by Edison in the presence of his laboratory workers. It was an exciting moment. While turning the crank attached to the cylinder, Edison shouted in the diaphragm the poem, "Mary Had a Little Lamb." The needle could be seen moving over the tin foil of the cylinder and leaving its

EARLY
COMMERCIAL
PHONOGRAPH

indentations. After moving the cylinder back, Edison turned the crank once more, and waited, fearing that nothing but unintelligible sounds would issue from his device. Instead, to the astonishment of everyone except the inventor, the words came faintly but quite audibly, just as Edison had spoken them. The modern phonograph was born.

Immediately the newspapers broadcast the news of the invention to an amazed world. Exhibitions were given all over the United States, creating a great deal of excitement. In his shops Edison manufactured many of the machines, which sold readily.

Edison fully realized the implications of his invention and clearly pictured the phonograph of the future. In an article in the *North American Review* for June, 1878, he set forth his conception of the way in which the phonograph would some day serve mankind. In addition to its simpler functions, such as its use for the reproduction of music and for purposes of education, he daringly predicted that some day the time would come when the phonograph would receive dictation and write letters without the aid of a stenographer, would play talking books for blind people, and would have other uses which seem marvelous even in our day.

THE DICTA-
PHONE IN USE—
DICTATION

THE DICTA-
PHONE IN USE—
TRANSCRIPTION

CONTRIBUTION OF OTHER INVENTORS

Because of his preoccupation with other useful inventions, Edison was not immediately able to perfect his original phonograph. A great difficulty was that the tin foil did not retain the needle indentations for any length of time, with the result that the recording was soon lost. In 1885 Bell and Tainter took a long step forward by substituting for the tin foil a cylinder of hard wax, upon which the needle cut long lines instead of indentations. Perhaps the greatest development came in 1877, as the contribution of Emil Berliner, who disregarded the cylinder altogether. The vibrations of the diaphragm were now recorded on a disc, revolving horizontally, in the form of a spiral. At first, Berliner's machine was called the gramophone, while Edison's product retained the name of phonograph. Much later, when Edison also began to manufacture the disc machines, the two names came to be used almost interchangeably.

The National Phonograph Company, founded by Edison, manufactured phonographs and cylindrical records on a huge scale. By 1897 Edison had sold over one and a half million phonographs and a hundred million records. For the first time in history people from all walks of life were able to satisfy their desire to hear music. For the first time good music became popular. In the humble cottage, among men posted in the far-off wilderness, as well as in the luxurious homes of the rich, great singers sang and world-famous orchestras played.

In addition to its function as entertainment, the phonograph has been put to a multitude of practical and scientific uses. The dictaphone has become a necessity in the modern business office, in the class room; foreign languages are taught by means of the phonograph. Most important of all, the speech and the music of great men and women, as well as their written words, may be preserved as valuable treasures for posterity.

MANY AN ANCIENT medicine man or magician has squatted hiding by the side of a mirror-like pool, hoping to see the reflections of his enemies as they passed by, confident he would be able to catch and keep those reflections, and make them serve his vengeful purposes.

When, in 1802, Wedgwood and Sir Humphrey Davy, two Englishmen, let the shadow of a man's head fall upon a piece of paper wet with silver nitrate, and tensely watched the paper turn slowly dark all around the edge of the shadow, they were not much more successful than the ancient medicine man at catching and keeping what they saw. They couldn't stop the whole paper from turning dark in a short time and so obliterating their crude silhouette. Moreover, the silhouette itself was a "negative"— white where it should be black, black where it should be white.

The human eye is a cleverly formed and versatile organ. It is sensitive to both very faint and strong illuminations; it faithfully records subtle variations of brightness and shadow; it can follow the swift flight of a bird or the slow movements of the hand of a watch; it translates the wave lengths of light into all the colors of the rainbow. Before photography, the only direct records man could have of events and persons were the sketches and portraits by artists. The story of photography is the story of man's attempt to duplicate the eye mechanically and, by so doing, to make things and events that only a few persons can see, available to all people. The experiments of Wedgwood and Davy were no more the beginning of this story than the end. They had made silhouettes but the human eye sees more than the mere outline of an object. Their chemical innovation had to be combined with a mechanical device, the camera.

Photo by, and courtesy of, Ed Wilcox

CANDID CAMERA SHOT OF A NIGHT CLUB ATTRACTION

XIII—20

Photo by Raeburn Rohrbach

BEAUTIFUL CLOUD EFFECTS OBTAINED THROUGH THE USE
OF A COLOR FILTER

Photo by Raeburn Rohrbach

WIRES AGAINST CLOUDS

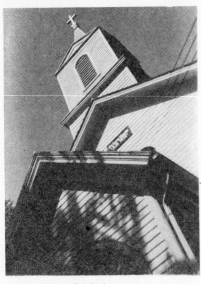

Photo by Raeburn Rohrbach

ANGULAR COMPOSITION

THE PINHOLE CAMERA

A learned Saracen of the twelfth century named Alhazan, the English monk Roger Bacon, Baptista Porta, and the artist Leonardo da Vinci, along with several others, all contributed to the invention and perfection of the pinhole camera. It was discovered that light, coming through a pinhole into a dark box, forms an image on the opposite side of the box. This image, except for being upside down and reversed, is a picture of what is in the light on the other side of the pinhole. Its accuracy is in proportion to the smallness of the hole. Not much light can come through. If the hole be enlarged, the picture blurs.

The human eye has a lens that corrects such blurring and so allows a larger amount of light to contribute to the image. A lens was put into the camera; and also a mirror to correct the reversal and inversion of the image. Thus the mechanical aspect of the eye was imitated, while Wedgwood and Davy very crudely duplicated the retina with their sensitive plate. Even in this, their work was by no means wholly original, but depended on the discovery of the German chemist, J. H. Schulze, that certain salts of silver are broken down and blackened by the action of light rather than that of heat.

The next step in the advance of photography was the combination of the sensitive plate and the camera. Humorously enough, it was partly effected by several artists, who were less renowned for their artistic ability than for the zeal with which they sought mechanical aids in their work.

In the early nineteenth century a Bavarian actor and dramatist named Senefelder decided he would have to become a printer if he were ever to succeed in getting his plays published. As an experiment, he tried to make printing blocks out of smooth stones by etching them with acid. One day his mother asked him to make out a laundry list and, having no pencil and paper, he wrote with a greasy crayon on one of his stones. Later he tried printing from the same stone—one gathers he was fond of such chance notions—and found that, if he first wet the stone, only the greasy crayon lines would take up the oily printers' ink. Thus he invented lithography.

This isolated discovery accidentally paved the way for a signal advance in photography. A Frenchman named Niepce became interested in the new art of printing pictures from stones. However, he could not draw, and so he attempted—rather stubbornly, it might seem—to get permanent pictures for his work by using a camera. In 1814 he coated a silver plate with asphaltum, placed it in a closed camera, focused an image upon it for several hours, then washed the plate in naptha. The amount of asphaltum that remained insoluble on each part of the plate was in proportion to the amount of light that had fallen there. He had a permanent picture—in which the high lights were represented by hardened asphaltum, and the shadows by silver. It was more like a negative than a positive image.

THE FIRST TINTYPES

Subsequently, Niepce was joined in his work by a painter named Daguerre. Together, they perfected the first of all tintypes, a silver plate coated with silver iodide which, when exposed to light in a camera and afterwards to mercury fumes, showed a permanent picture whose shadows were dark and whose high lights were bright; in short, a "positive." It was a considerable ordeal to sit for these first daguerreotypes. The person whose picture was being taken had to sit motionless in bright sunlight for at least five minutes. Moreover, since the plate itself became the photograph, there was no way of duplicating it; each picture had to be posed separately.

At about the same time the first daguerreotypes were being framed, another artist was seeking mechanical aids for his work. An Englishman named Fox Talbot was using a form of camera to help him make drawings of natural objects at Lake Como. This camera was arranged to cast an image on a sheet of white paper; the artist had then to trace the form of the image with pencil or paints, which is not as easy a task as it sounds. Talbot began to wonder if he could not eliminate the tedious pencil work. He knew that Sir John Herschel had discovered that hydrosulphites will dissolve various salts of silver. So he proceeded to make permanent negatives after the manner of Wedgwood and Davy, using a camera and preserving the prints by washing out the residual silver salts with hydrosulphites. He prevented his negatives from becoming completely black with the passage of time. But he also went a step further. He made such negatives on very thin paper, oiled them to increase transparency, laid them on top of other clean sheets wet with silver salts, and exposed the whole to sunlight. The picture he thus made on the sheet underneath was bright where the one on top was dark, dark where the one on top was bright. Fox Talbot had made a permanent picture that duplicated the lights and shadows of nature; in short, a permanent positive. Moreover, he was able to make any number of pictures from one negative. He had brought mass production into the field of photography. Talbot's process, which he called calotype, was the keystone of modern photography, whereas

LITHUANIAN
FISHERMAN'S
HOME

The camera's accurate record spreads visual information throughout the world.

Black Star photo
By Dr Gutschow
(U. S. Pictures)

HOMING PIGEON
IN FLIGHT
A photograph made in
1/50,000 second, taken
just after the bird was
launched in flight, and
showing every detail
as plainly as in a still
picture.

Courtesy Massachusetts
Institute of Technology

the inventions of Niepce and Daguerre turned out to be no more than mentally stimulating bypaths, outmoded today. The year 1839 saw the publishing of both processes. The human eye had been partially duplicated.

NEW REFINEMENTS

Thereafter came a host of refinements. Niepce's earliest pictures on asphaltum had to be exposed for six hours before the picture appeared; he could only photograph stationary objects. Talbot's calotype reduced the exposure time needed to three minutes. Later investigations showed that the sensitivity of the plate, in other words, the swiftness with which the picture appeared, depended upon the medium in which the silver salts were held. Glass plates coated with albumen were substituted for wet paper, giving the added advantage of greater transparency. Later collodion and collodion emulsion were substituted for albumen. Finally, in 1871, Dr. R. L. Maddox successfully used gelatine for the same purpose, thereby giving to photography a material upon which it has never essentially improved. Exposures of a fraction of a second were made possible. Coincidentally, the dry gelatine film eliminated the necessity of preparing a wet plate immediately before taking a picture and washing and developing it immediately after. Since 1890 amateur photography has become progressively less complicated, and mass manufacture became general.

Another matter in which the photographic plate was made to

mimic the retina of the eye was that of the wave-lengths of light to which it was sensitive. Of all the range of vibration between the cosmic ray and the radio wave, the human eye sees only a small median fraction. The early camera was very sensitive to the wave lengths we see as blue and violet, and hardly sensitive at all to yellow and red. To it, geraniums and sunflowers were black, violets were white, hazel eyes were black eyes, blue eyes were colorless. In 1873, H. W. Vogel of Berlin discovered that if photographic plates were immersed in certain dyes, their sensitivity to the colors at the red end of the spectrum was increased. Further improvements were made in this process until, by 1906, it was possible to manufacture "pan-chromatic" plates that neatly duplicated the eye's range of vision, though not its ability to see the various colors themselves.

COLOR PHOTOGRAPHY

This color problem was a difficult one. It offered no immediate solution, no simple method of photographing colors onto a plate, as was possible with lights and shadows. Each color seemed to present a different problem. However, a method of simplification was found. It is a well-known fact that all colors can be built up as combinations of the three primaries: red, blue, and yellow. Catch those colors and you catch them all. If an object or scene be photographed through blue glass only those things that are colored blue, or some color in which blue appears, such as green or violet, will register on the plate. The same will hold true for the photographs made through red and yellow glass.

Fotograms, N. Y.

GEORGE EASTMAN

Printing plates can then be designed from the three photographs, and the three primary colors impressed in turn on one sheet of paper. The three views will fit together precisely, colors other than the primaries being produced by combinations, blue and yellow making green, yellow and red making orange. In 1861 the English physicist, Clerk Maxwell, made the first color photograph by this method focusing it on a screen from three separate projectors, one for each primary hue.

In the early days of color photography it was only possible to depict a stationary object, since three successive photographs had to be made. Later, prisms were devised to split up the light entering the camera into three different paths, each reaching a different plate at the same time.

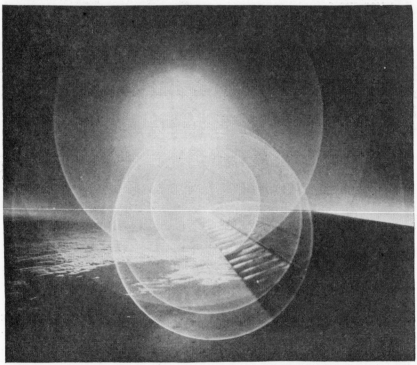

Courtesy American Museum of Natural History, N. Y.

AN EXAMPLE OF "FREAK" PHOTOGRAPHY
This picture of an eclipse of the sun, made from a plane at 25,000 feet altitude, shows a series of circular rings caused by reflection between the several surfaces of the lens. Incidentally, the clouds in lower left are 22,000 feet below the plane.

Courtesy American Museum of Science, N. Y.

SIXTEEN SUCCESSIVE EXPOSURES OF AN ECLIPSE OF THE SUN

With photography's conquest of color the science was able to boast that it could, with ever increasing accuracy, catch and record anything that the human eye could see. But it did not stop there. It began to see more than the human eye.

GOING BEYOND THE HUMAN EYE

The camera can see things that are too faint for the eye to perceive, even when aided by instruments. Attached to a telescope, it records the images of distant stars and far-off nebulae, tracks down dim, shifting comets, and accurately records the appearance of whole sectors of the heavens. This is partly due to the extreme sensitivity of the plates and partly to its ability to focus on a star or comet for hours, following it across the sky without winking or fatigue.

The camera can respond to wave lengths of light too long or short for the human eye. It can see and record the X-rays that

THE PARIS WORLD'S EXPOSITION AT NIGHT (1937)

penetrate and silhouette the interiors of opaque objects and the inner organs and bones of men and animals. Its mechanical eye was from the days of Wedgwood and Davy especially sensitive to wave lengths of light just beyond the blue end of vision, the ultra-violet rays. It helped to prove their invisible existence. Now it uses them to detect forgeries and read ancient writings that have been erased and written over, and to photograph, through high powered microscopes, objects so small that their form cannot be transmitted by coarser light.

The camera is selective. By means of filters, it can ignore all colors but one. Red and infra-red are less disturbed by haze and fog than are the shorter wave lengths. A special camera can filter out the latter and show distinct objects where there is apparently only a blurring mist.

The camera can see objects that are moving too swiftly for the human eye to focus. Not only roaring automobiles, and race horses pounding down to a neck and neck "photographic" finish, and the swift throw of a baseball pitcher, but also the trajectory of a bullet, the lightning-like movements of machinery, and the stages in the breaking of a soap bubble, can all be magically arrested and held up to view.

Photo by Gottfried Hinker, Vienna

ARTISTIC COMPOSITION IN PHOTOGRAPHY

Courtesy Eastman Kodak Co.

PICTURES SHOWING RESULTS OBTAINED WITH INFRA-RED FILTER
Above: Photo without using the filter; below, the same scene with filter used.

The camera can record, in less than a second, complicated scenes that the eye would have to focus many times. Given a few preliminary measurements, land can be surveyed and maps made by means of sets of photographs taken from stationary positions and from airplanes. Legal documents, checks, art objects, and stars, all can pass under the infallible eye. Criminal and celebrity alike cannot escape the knowing wink of the candid camera which, supplementing and in certain ways transcending the human eye, is watching everywhere.

Courtesy Massachusetts Institute of Technology

A PANE OF GLASS AT THE INSTANT
IT IS SHATTERED BY A BULLET

CONSIDER WHAT THE WORLD and especially the minds of its people would be, had they gone through the first third of the twentieth century without the motion picture. Many compartments in those minds would be tenantless, or occupied by different tenants. Micky Mouse and Pop Eye and their jolly, grotesque company would never have been, or would have confined their mad antics to the staid, motionless media of books and comic supplements. The glamorous, unreachable "stars"—the gods and goddesses of modern fable—would never have loved and striven before their millions of observers, or touched off the fires of hopeless, day-dreaming romance. The habits of gesticulation and carriage of presidents, kings, and dictators, the quirks of expression of politicians and diplomats, of leading business men and labor leaders, would not be the matters of public knowledge that the news reels have made them. Football games, peace conferences, campaign speeches, and bathing beauty contests would remain a matter of hearsay or newspaper report. Schools and workshops would still be limited to the book, the blackboard and the map. The kaleidoscopic realm of Hollywood, sometimes realistic, sometimes grandiose, would not be the weekly fare of most people, would not be shaping the minds of adults and children. In short, action and movement would not be enlivening news, education, and amusement.

For centuries man has sought to make a pictorial representation of motion. Some Egyptian tomb drawings have a marked similarity to serial cartoons. Certain early Italian paintings tell their story by naïvely combining several actions into one. But the final conquest of the problem had its practical beginning, strangely enough, in toys—toys conceived and constructed during the latter half of the nineteenth century, toys that depended for their working upon a function of the human eye called persistence of vision.

PERSISTENCE OF VISION

When we are riding in an automobile past a fence that has cracks in it, we seem to see through the fence as if it were no more than a gauze screen; when we wink our eyes we don't have any definite impression of blackness; when a lighted match is whirled in the dark we see a track of light; the same thing happens when the gigantic spark that is lightning shoots across the sky. This is because the sensitive retina of the eye does not react instantaneously to changes; after an object disappears, it still sees that object for about one sixteenth of a second. So, if a number of separate pictures, each representing a slightly different phase of the same action, be presented successively and swiftly, they will appear to the eye as a continuous action. This effect can be demonstrated very simply by ruffling cards with slowly changing pictures drawn on them. Sir John Herschel made a cardboard disc with a bird depicted on one side and a cage on the other. When the disc was twirled by means of strings attached to the sides, both pictures were seen at once; the bird appeared to be in the cage.

The first attempts to devise a machine that would give the same effect in a little more sophisticated form were of necessity crude. A description of one will illustrate them all. In the middle of the nineteenth century two Europeans, Dr. Joseph Plateau and Dr. Simon von Stampfer, improving on the mechanism of the Englishman, Roget, mounted a series of pictures on the outside rim of a wheel on a horizontal axis. In a circular screen just outside the wheel was a slot through which the pictures could be observed. The wheel was revolved.

Courtesy Bell & Howell Co.

A SMALL (8MM.) MOTION-PICTURE CAMERA

Courtesy Bell & Howell Co.

16MM. MOTOR-DRIVEN MOTION-
PICTURE CAMERA WITH THREE
LENSES

As each picture came fully into view it snapped a shutter that caused it to be momentarily illuminated from behind. The device was successful but, at the time, there was no practical way of developing it further. The pictures it used were drawn laboriously by hand, since the art of photography was only in its initial stages. The flexible film was not in use, so the cycle of action that could be presented was limited by the size of the wheel. Moreover, each individual picture was seen while in motion; this caused a blurring effect very tiring to the eyes. The only immediate practical result of the invention of Plateau and Stampfer was a toy version, the zoetrope.

The motion picture is an invention whose central idea has been hit upon by many men. Even its most modern refinements, such as colored photography, the steady movement of the film rather than movement by jerks, and synchronized sound, were all anticipated in crude forms by early investigators. Plateau himself planned a stereoptican apparatus that would show movement in three dimensions—something that has not even today been made practical on a commercial scale. The only thing that held such men back was the lack of suitable equipment materials. Until these were sufficiently developed, no long, forward strides could be taken.

So we can pass over the many small improvements that were made in the zoetrope in the next few decades, the many versions of the machine that were constructed by separate independent investigators. It would be, for the most part, only an interesting story of blind alleys. Not until the last decades of the nineteenth century did the crucial materials come into use.

ALL FOUR HOOFS OFF THE GROUND

By 1870 photographic plates had been devised that were of sufficient sensitivity to take a picture if exposed for only the thousandth part of a second. Two years later Governor Leland Stanford of California wagered certain horse-racing enthusiasts that a trotting horse gets all its feet off the ground at one stage in its stride. A wealthy man, Stanford commissioned John Isaacs, an engineer, and Edward Muybridge, a photographer, to try to solve the problem. They set up a series of cameras along the racing course on Stanford's stock farm in Palo Alto. From the trigger of each camera a thread was stretched taut across the track. The horse, in going by, snapped its own pictures. Stanford won his bet; Muybridge went on photographing other phases of the movement of animals and men, and awakened considerable popular interest in the subject.

Courtesy Bell & Howell Co.

16MM. MOTION-PICTURE PROJECTOR

At about the same time, a French painter named Meissonier was in the midst of a heated controversy as to whether the postures of the horses in his pictures were natural. He borrowed Muybridge's pictures and, as a final proof of his contention, set them up on a device similar to the zoetrope, projected them onto a screen, and so synthesized them. Like Stanford, he was victorious in his controversy. Various scientists became interested in the method. The Frenchman, Dr. E. J. Marey, conferred with Muybridge, and afterwards constructed what he called a photographic gun, with which he too was able to take pictures of birds in flight, of cats falling and righting themselves, and of other animals in action. The Englishman, W. E. Greene, and the American, Wallace Levinson, did the same. The public was hungry for motion. One of Greene's window displays attracted such a crowd that the police forced him to discontinue these pictures. The problem of making clear-cut pictures of swift action was solved.

The second piece of equipment necessary for the successful production of motion pictures on a large scale was a film that was at once flexible, durable, strong, transparent, and easily sensitized for photographic purposes. Paper was tried and was successful for ordinary uses, as in cameras that took one picture at a time: but it was too fragile and crumpled too easily when run at the high, jerky speeds necessary for motion picture photography and projection. But in 1885 Hannibal Goodwin discovered celluloid, one of the many derivatives of deadly gun-cotton. It was obviously an ideal material for the purpose. By 1889 George Eastman was manufacturing it in the United States.

During these years since the making of the zoetrope, the electric light and arc light had been invented, electricity was coming into common use, and there had been improvements in the making of accurate machinery. All the necessary materials and equipment had been assembled. Only an inventor who would apply the materials was wanting.

EDISON AND JENKINS

Thomas A. Edison was trying to build a motion-picture machine to use in conjunction with his phonograph. At first he

MOTION-PICTURE
PROJECTOR WITH
SOUND EQUIP-
MENT

Courtesy Holmes
Projector Co.

tried to model it after the phonograph, mounting microscopic pictures spirally on a cylinder, rotating the cylinder, and
viewing the pictures through a magnifier. Finding this impractical, he built a machine in which the separate pictures were
mounted on a tape or belt. Eastman's film, coming into existence
at a convenient time, solved the problem of the proper material
for the belt.

Edison's first moving pictures were taken in a small tar-paper
studio called "The Black Maria." Three vaudeville teams did their
turns, boxers and fencers gave exhibitions, trained bears were displayed, along with other novelties suitable for silent performance
in a confined space. Edison's first projection device, the kineto-

Courtesy R. K. O.

SCENE FROM "QUALITY STREET"

scope, was essentially a highly improved zoetrope that took advantage of all the new materials; in short, a peep-show. The
single observer put his eyes to an opening; the film unwound
continuously before him; each picture as it passed was momentarily illuminated by an electric spark that vanished almost instantaneously. Sometimes as many as forty-eight images were
viewed in a second. The performance lasted for about thirteen
seconds; if you got something in your eye, you missed the whole
show.

But the kinetoscope did not satisfy one condition essential for
giving a clear-cut illusion of motion: the individual pictures were
not absolutely at rest while being viewed. By 1894 C. Francis
Jenkins, among others, had built a camera that took care of this
difficulty. Jenkins was a stenographer in the Treasury Department attached to the Coast Guard; he experimented in his spare
time, fabricating many of his own materials and splicing his own

film. In his camera, the film, controlled by a sprocket that engaged a line of perforations along the edge, moved in a series of
jerks. A ratchet and pawl mechanism allowed each individual picture to rest for a fraction of a second when being projected. While
the pictures were changing, a shutter momentarily obscured them.
In this way Jenkins took the motion out of motion pictures, and
began the conquest of the flicker.

So, by 1895, the general form of the motion picture camera
and projector was fixed upon, and the period of refinement and
commercialization begun. The time that each individual picture
held the screen was increased, the dark period between was cut
down. It became a general practice to project the pictures on a
screen, so enabling a large audience to view them. The French
brothers, the Lumières, sent men all over the world to photograph far places and people. An Edison cameraman began packing all the thrilling tricks of photography into such one-reel

Courtesy Metro-Goldwyn-Mayer

SCENE FROM THE MOTION PICTURE "GOOD EARTH"

Courtesy Metro-Goldwyn-Mayer

SCENE FROM THE MOTION PICTURE "GOOD EARTH"

Photo by Techni-Photo, N. Y.

VISUAL EDUCATION
The motion picture is coming into use in the classroom.

stories as *The Life of an American Fireman* and *The Great Train Robbery*. Moving pictures, as we know them today, got underway.

"TALKIES"

Edison first conceived of his motion pictures as talking pictures, accompanying them by a synchronized phonograph. But sound had also to wait for the right materials, for improvements in the methods of recording, for the development of amplification, for the photoelectric cell. By the end of the first quarter of the twentieth century they were ready. In 1926 "Vitaphone" was successfully demonstrated, a realization of Edison's original design to synchronize the movements of a photographic film and a phonographic needle. A little later, with the aid of the photoelectric cell, a much closer combination of the two was worked out. A beam of light, controlled by a photocell, that varied in intensity, according to the pitch and quality of the voices, noises, and musical notes being recorded, was allowed to fall on a moving, narrow strip of sensitive film. When the film was developed it showed, in general, a series of alternately dark and light transverse bands. The relative crowding of these bands represented the pitch of the sound; their shape, the quality; their brightness, the loudness or intensity. When a beam of light was sent back through the light track on the developed film, it activated a photoelectric cell, and a current which varied in the same way as the light was produced. This was amplified and re-produced through a loud-speaker the original sounds.

Sometimes, as in direct newsreel reporting, the picture and sound recordings are made in the same camera, on the same film. More usually the two are made simultaneously, but in separate machines, the narrow sound track being afterwards transferred to the edge of the film. In either case, they run as one when projected.

The first sound pictures were relatively as cramped as those reels made in the "Black Maria;" the outdoor scenes, and distance and angle shots had all temporarily to be discarded in order to pamper the delicate microphone. Today the new problem is well solved. The microphone, attached by a telescopic neck to a high framework that moves on rubber tires, follows the actors about like an inquisitive dinosaur. If the words it hears are mispro-

Paul's Photos, Chicago

LOUIS LUMIERE, FRENCH INVENTOR, DEMONSTRATING HIS
NEW STEREOSCOPIC FILM

Courtesy Bell & Howell Co.

BIG AND LITTLE GET THE SAME SHOT

In the background a 35mm. motion picture camera is shooting a scene on location, while the director, in the foreground with his own small movie camera, is "stealing" a scene for his own library.

nounced or slurred, they can later be removed from the sound track and corrections "dubbed in." Soundproof studios big enough to house castles and small armies have been built. All the motors that run the camera and the sound track have become noiseless. The moving picture as well as the microphone has made advances; "process shots" are photographed hundreds of miles away from the studio, then projected in the studio with actors in front of them, and realistically rephotographed. Natural, life-like colors are being developed and introduced.

All these achievements are the result of the original notion, which many clever men independently conceived, and of the ingenious use of the right materials, achievements calling forth the efforts of a whole horde of experimenters and investigators.

OUR CIVILIZATION RESTS ON steel. Modern industrial as well as agricultural life would be impossible without it. Locomotives, factories, automobiles, skyscrapers, and a million other necessities are inseparable parts of the fascinating story of steel.

While the processing of steel is of recent origin, iron has been known to man for ages past. It has been said that Sir Walter Raleigh, great English adventurer, triumphantly brought samples of iron from Virginia to England. But he was not by any means the discoverer of this ore. In the great pyramid of Gizeh, iron remnants have been found which were placed there by ancient Egyptians six thousand years ago.

Iron ore, as found under the earth's surface, consists of a simple combination of iron, oxygen, and various impurities. The ore, essentially, is simply iron rust, formed because of the great affinity which iron has for the oxygen in the air. In order to obtain the metal, the oxygen has to be eliminated from the iron ore, and carbon substituted in its place. In the past, this was accomplished by a crude process. Ore was thrown into heaps of burning charcoal. Because of the heat, the ore melted, the oxygen separated, and the carbon from the charcoal united with the residue. The resulting product, after it had cooled, was smelted iron, but of a poor quality. Before the iron had cooled entirely, it was usually hammered out into the desired thinness and shape.

In the Middle Ages furnaces were substituted for the open fire, so that greater heat could be produced and the iron more easily melted. By 1600 the blast furnace came into general use and was employed in England to make large quantities of iron. By means of huge bellows blowing air into the furnace, the heat was increased. About the same time Dud Dudley first used coke in place of charcoal, the coke that is now so necessary to the mass production of iron and steel.

Courtesy Hibbing, Minnesota, Chamber of Commerce

AN OPEN PIT IRON MINE

As ore is removed, tracks accommodating the ore trains are laid at successively lower levels.

The name of Henry Cort is closely associated with two other improvements. He originated what came to be known as the "Puddling Furnace." Coal or coke contains an amount of sulphur which, when mixed with iron, causes the latter to become brittle. Cort set out to make a furnace of two compartments, separating the coal and iron. The huge flame emanating from the coal would blow into the iron heaped on a separate hearth, melting it rapidly. In Cort's day every piece of iron had to be hammered out by hand, a laborious and expensive task. He conceived the idea of passing the hot iron through a series of iron rolls, thus rolling the metal into its required shape and thinness. This rolling mill permitted the production of iron in large quantities and cheaply, thus bringing it into more general use.

Steel was not made in Europe until the eighteenth century. Then, because of its toughness and hardness, it was used for the manufacture of tools and machinery, as it is today. This steel was known as "crucible steel." Pure iron, that is, iron without carbon,

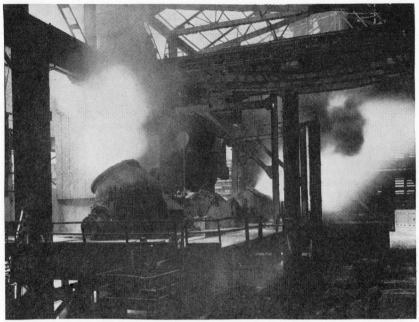

Courtesy Carnegie-Illinois Steel Corporation. Photo by Fred'G. Korth, Chicago

BESSEMER CONVERTERS IN ACTION

The metal in the nearest vessel shows a flame typical of the middle of the blow while the flame in the farthest vssel shows that the metal is ready for pouring.

called wrought iron, together with some charcoal, was placed in a furnace, and kept hot for as long a period as six weeks. As can readily be imagined, the resulting product of this crude method was very expensive.

BESSEMER, FATHER OF MODERN STEEL

To Bessemer goes the credit for one of the greatest discoveries of recent times. But for him, the modern Steel Age might not have occurred, at least it would have been postponed.

Invention was the life task of this Englishman. He invented a stamping machine and contributed to the science of war by improving cannon and by substituting the long projectile for the round cannon ball. As he developed the long projectile, he soon realized that a better type of steel was needed to strengthen the barrel of the cannon. Using his own money, he continually experimented with iron and metals to accomplish this purpose.

One day he quite accidentally noticed that the inside of a bar or "pig" of iron melted more readily than the iron on the outside. His imagination stimulated, Bessemer immediately set out to investigate this curious phenomenon. He knew that iron containing a high percentage of carbon melted more readily. Hence he concluded that the outside of the bar must have lost its carbon content. The great question was how this had come about. He surmised that hot air currents in the furnace had driven out the carbon.

Bessemer began his experimentation. He tried blowing air into a crucible filled with molten iron. He had expected that this would cool the iron, but to his surprise this simple procedure increased the heat inside the crucible several times. The air, combining with the carbon, manganese, and silicon of the iron, caused combustion and intense heat. Bessemer was overcome with joy, for he had discovered the cheapest fuel that could possibly be found, that is, air.

In 1856 Bessemer read a paper to the Royal Institute of England—"On the Manufacture of Steel without Fuel." When some steel manufacturers tried to apply this method, it proved to be a total failure and Bessemer was discredited. After some years of experimentation, however, the cause of the difficulty was found. The pig iron used by the manufacturers was too low in manganese content, and contained too much phosphorus. The result was a brittle steel product. Since then, manganese and other materials have been added to the molten iron and several refinements of the simple Bessemer process introduced. This made possible the cheap manufacture of steel and the existence of the modern world.

LONG ago, too far back in forgotten centuries to be recorded in history, an unknown inventor made a water wheel. The principle involved was simple: the running water was directed against paddles or blades arranged on a wheel. By turning part of a stream into a trough, the water could be made to flow against the blades of a vertical wheel. The shaft or axle, turning at slow or high speed, thus developed enough power to drive various machines, such as mills to grind grain. If the wheel were located below a fall in the stream bed, the descending water exerted considerable force when it fell on the blades or buckets fixed on the rim.

FROM WATER WHEEL TO TURBINE

The first turbine was a water wheel enclosed in a casing. Fixed blades directed the water against the wheel. This invention was the work of a Frenchman, Benoît Fourneyron, in 1823. About sixty years later, Charles Pelton made a tangential water wheel having buckets against which the water was shot from a nozzle. Particularly applicable to great waterfalls which have a high "head," the Pelton wheel has enjoyed wide application. About 30,000 horse-power may be developed by generators run by the Pelton wheel.

Water turbines have been installed at the sources of power on rivers, near waterfalls, and in huge dams. Transmission lines carry the electric current to centers of population for use in factories, stores, and homes. At Muscle Shoals, Alabama, there are huge water turbines in the Wilson Dam. Above this plant is the Norris Dam, capable of producing twice as much electrical power as the Wilson Dam. On the Colorado River, water turbines with a potential production of about 1,800,000 horse-power will be installed in Boulder Dam.

CROSS SECTION
OF A 13,500 H.P.
TURBINE

Courtesy the Allis-
Chalmers Mfg. Co.

Sometime in the second century B. C., probably about the year 123, an Alexandrian Greek named Hero described a wheel which could be moved by steam ejected from tubes. At Padua many centuries later, Branca made plans for an engine which was operated by directing steam against a wheel. Then came Newcomen, Watt, and other inventors. The steam engine using a reciprocating piston served very well in various industrial capacities, in spite of the fact that it was expensive, cumbersome, and inefficient. But a rotary engine was needed, one which did not depend upon a piston for developing power. This need was particularly acute, especially when the dynamo, requiring high speeds, was invented. The steam turbine soon appeared with the answer to the demand for a rotary engine.

Many mechanical geniuses contributed to the invention of the

Courtesy Allis-Chalmers Mfg. Co.

ROTOR OF A STEAM TURBINE

steam turbine. One of the first of these inventors was Charles A. Parsons, the son of an English nobleman who won fame as a telescope builder. Young Parsons received his education from private tutors and intimate contact with machines. After many tedious experiments, Parsons demonstrated his steam turbine in 1884. This turbine, which developed only ten horse-power, had an efficiency of thirty per cent, three times that of the recipro- cating steam engine. Parsons constructed a series of fixed and moving blades or vanes enclosed in a long cylinder. The moving blades were on discs that revolved between the blades fixed on the inside of the cylinder. The steam, broken up into small jets, was directed against the curved blades of the first disc. It then passed on to react against the fixed blades, curved in the opposite direc- tion. Forced from disc to disc, the expansive power of the steam turned them with great speed. Here was a device that could be used to run the dynamos. But since its speed was so great, im- proved generators had to be built.

PERFECTION OF THE STEAM TURBINE

Parsons was not alone in the field. A Swedish inventor, Gustaf de Laval, built a single-wheel steam turbine in 1889. In the rim of a wheel he cut vanes against which nozzles blew steam under high pressure. The disc was enclosed in a sealed casing to prevent too great a loss in efficiency. Shooting at a speed of 4,000 feet per second, the jets of steam forced De Laval's five-inch wheel to make 30,000 revolutions per minute. Much of the expansive power of steam used in a De Laval turbine is lost. In the Parsons engine, it is necessary to have a large number of blades. There is a clearance of about three one-hundredths of an inch between the fixed and rotating blades. Expansion due to heat, and other contingencies, may result in serious damage to such an engine.

Charles E. Curtis of New York combined the inventions of Parsons and De Laval to overcome the weaknesses of each. He used sets of De Laval discs revolving in separate chambers. Between the discs he placed a pressure compartment. After delivering a driving impulse to the first disc, the steam is forced into a pressure chamber and then passes on, at a lower pressure, through nozzles to another disc. The speed of this type of turbine may be controlled easily by shutting off some of the nozzles and allowing the steam to escape. After having spent some $60,000 on his experiments, Curtis sold his rights to a concern which spent $3,000,-000 on perfecting the engine.

The steam turbine is a remarkable application of coal or other fuel to the generation of electricity. Combustion produces heat which converts water to steam. Super-heated to 706° F., steam exerts a pressure of 3,000 pounds per square inch. Emmett, employed by the company which bought Curtis' turbine, in 1912 began experiments with mercury to overcome some of the disadvantages of using water heated by coal. Mercury, which boils at 677° F., can store more heat and so do more work than boiling water. Emmett's researches were shown to be a success when in 1923 the Hartford Electric Light and Power Company installed generators driven by mercury vapor turbines developing 6,000 horse-power.

BUCKET WHEEL FOR 30,000 H.P. UNITS
The assembled wheel for a water turbine weighs 25 tons.

Courtesy Union Pacific Railroad
THE FOUR INTAKE TOWERS AT BOULDER DAM
The towers are 375 feet high, and control the flow of water into the turbines.

A FASCINATING ENGINE

This new departure in turbines is a fascinating engine. Ordinary fuel is used to boil the mercury which vaporizes at 677° F., and produces a pressure of 35 pounds per square inch. The vapor is carried to a single-stage turbine which turns a generator. Then it passes through condensing coils where the temperature decreases to 455°, and back to the mercury tank to be vaporized again. While going through these coils, arranged in a boiler, the mercury is still hot enough to convert the surrounding water to steam. Nozzles direct this steam to a Curtis turbine which turns another generator. Mercury vapor is a deadly poison, so it is absolutely essential that the vapor turbine, coils, and boiler be hermetically sealed. Almost unbelievable efficiency is obtained from Emmett's mercury turbine.

There is a long gap between Hero's simple steam engine or the primitive water wheel and the awe-inspiring turbines now in use. Gigantic steam and water turbines developing thousands of horsepower, housed in power plants, or mounted in ocean liners, have been of incalculable importance in making this an electrical age.

MORE than iron, coal or steam, the clock is indispensible to modern civilization. Science could replace the basic materials of industrial society, but the clock is irreplaceable as the instrument which regulates the complexity of contemporary life.

The modern mechanical clock was invented with the dawn of the Machine Age. As it came into popular use, it brought about that efficiency and order that marked the principal difference between feudal and industrial society. The concept of eternity dominated life in feudal days. With the coming of the clock, time was carefully measured and all the activities of life—eating, sleeping, work, recreation — were regulated by it. Time became a commodity.

THE SUNDIAL
Probably the earliest form of timepiece.

MARKING THE HOURS

Clocks were first used to systematize daily routine in the monasteries in the thirteenth century. These were largely water clocks (the Clepsydra of ancient Greece), and in their simplest form they involved little or no mechanism. The hours were sounded by a simple device which dropped a ball into a bronze gong or blew a reed trumpet.

But in palaces and cathedrals water clocks were often among the most elaborate pieces of decoration. They were designed as

puppet theaters, with tiny figures enacting playlets at the
sounding of the hours. They
were supplemented by mechanisms which displayed the movement of sun, moon, and stars.
When the mechanical timepiece
was invented, marionette clocks
were developed more imagina-
tively. One of the best of these
is the fourteenth-century clock
still marking the hours at Strass-
burg.

It was the introduction of
the gear principle into the mechanism of timekeeping that
made possible the mechanical
clock. Gears had been common

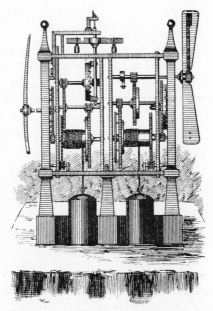

DE WICK'S CLOCK (1370)

since the pre-Christian period, chiefly in the milling industry.
Their use in clocks was made possible by a French scientist's
invention of a crude escapement device which would control
the force of a falling weight, making it move at an accelerating
speed.

The early clocks were made at the anvil of a general smithy
with a technique developed in work on mill gears, and were in-
evitably strange combinations of brilliance in conception and
deficiency in physical execution. It was only after several centuries of refinement in mechanism that the modern toolmaker
replaced the blacksmith.

In the thirteenth and fourteenth centuries clocks were built
in the towers of St. Paul's and Westminster in London and in the
cathedrals at Exeter, Peterborough, Norwich, Beauvais and a
dozen other towns. That in Peterborough still resembles its original
state since its restoration in 1836. England led in clockmaking,
but France, Switzerland, Italy and Germany were her close rivals.

Indeed, so skilled were French clockmakers that it is strange Charles V should have imported a German, Heinrich von Wick (he has gone down in history by his French appellation, de Vick) to design the clock at the Royal Palace in Paris in 1344. De Vick's timepiece represents the height of the first period of the mechanical clock. It embodied the essential principles of clockmaking and the finest details of the era, but it is so naïve and crude that in comparison with modern instruments it would scarcely be called a clock.

LIFE REGULATED BY THE CLOCK

Charles's timepiece also broke the monasteries' monopoly of timekeeping and made the clock the guiding instrument of the layman's life. Charles ordered the hours and quarter-hours to be struck by all churches in Paris according to the time given by the Palace clock, and in Vincennes according to the Château clock. He established equal hours in place of the variable hours recorded by the water clock, which had taken over the measurements of the sun dial. Days began to be counted by twelve hours from noon to midnight. Clocks ruled the activities of the merchants and artisans, who were beginning to replace the feudal lords and farmers as the dominant classes.

In imitation of Paris, tower clocks sprang up in towns all over Europe. Elaborate timepieces also became an accepted part of cathedrals, where some of the best marionette and astronomical mechanisms were constructed. Domestic clocks and pocket watches were owned only by the wealthy.

In the fifteenth century clocks which showed the minutes and seconds were introduced in Germany and the march toward accuracy was begun. Clocks began to be used by astronomers and other scientists for delicate work.

It was the invention of the pendulum in the second half of the seventeenth century that solved the problem of precision. The Arabs of Spain are said to have used the pendulum as early as the beginning of the eleventh century. Its real history begins with Leonardo da Vinci, and Italian engineering of the sixteenth

Courtesy The Art Institute of Chicago

17TH CENTURY ENGLISH CLOCKS

Courtesy The Art Institute of Chicago

A HOODED MURAL CLOCK OF
THE 17TH CENTURY

century, when it was used to produce reciprocating motion in pumps. It was applied to timekeeping by Galileo and Huygens. Prior to that time, timepieces had been really trustworthy only for measuring the transit between meridians. With the pendulum it was possible to adjust them for greater accuracy.

During the period that clocks were being perfected, discovery of the use of springs in the driving mechanism of timepieces gave new accuracy to the pocket watch and the portable clock. The early pocket watch reached its height in the "Nuremberg egg," a pendant-shaped watch made in Germany. Portable clocks developed into the table and mantel types. During the second quarter of the eighteenth century, the balance spring was invented, giving almost absolute precision to the watch as the pendulum had given it to the clock. The wrist watch has brought constantly increasing refinements to its delicate mechanism.

Clocks indicating solar time played an important part in timekeeping between the fourteenth and seventeenth centuries. In the latter part of this era, clocks showing solar time were as generally used as mechanical clocks. In the fourteenth century, pocket sundials were as frequently carried by wealthy and fashionable young men as pocket watches.

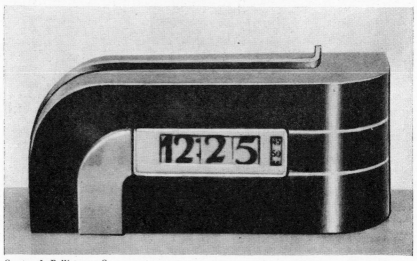

Courtesy L. E. Waterman Co.

A SPEEDOMETER STYLE DESK CLOCK

Courtesy Waterbury Clock Co.

SCHEMATIC EXHIBIT SHOWING STEPS IN THE MANUFACTURE OF
AN ALARM CLOCK

The seventeenth and eighteenth centuries saw the development of the chronometer, a marine clock used for measuring longitude. Today the chronometer is one of the most accurate and ingeniously constructed clocks. Its balance wheel is compensated for variations of temperature, it is insulated from magnetic attraction and it is hung in a special frame to prevent the ship's motion from disturbing its mechanism.

TIMEKEEPERS MARCH ON

Since the perfection of the mechanism, the chief developments in timekeeping have been the evolution of beauty and grace in cases, and the development of the electric clock. England and France have excelled in decorative work. English clocks were given grace by fit proportion and the use of finely-grained woods. The French created timepieces of dazzling splendor, executed in gilt bronze or cast in gilded metal or marble in combination. The alarm clock has symbolized the application of modern ingenuity for gadgets to the household clock.

In the electric clock, electricity has brought the precision of an observatory clock to the ordinary office or household timepiece.

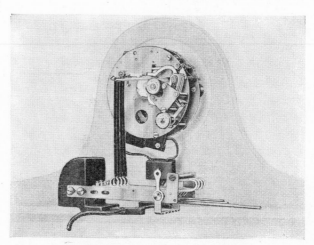

SELF-STARTING CHIME MOVEMENT

Some of these clocks are controlled by a timepiece in an astronomical observatory. The pendulum of the controlling clock, in swinging to either side, makes a brief contact, which completes the circuit of a galvanic battery and sends a current to the controlled clock. The currents pass through a coil in the bob of the pendulum and the action between these currents and a pair of fixed magnets forces the pendulum to one side and to the other alternately. The effect is that though the controlled clock may permanently continue to be a fraction of a second in advance of the master clock, it can never be so much as a half second in advance.

The popular electric clocks in homes and offices, however, are controlled by the impulse regulator in the generating station from which the clock receives its electricity. These are usually sixty-cycle alternating current clocks.

The hourly broadcasts of correct astronomical time throughout the nation by the United States Naval Observatory stations have brought new accuracy to ordinary mechanical clocks.

As civilization grows more complex, mechanical ingenuity has made the clock more accurate, and the efficiency and order which the first crude mechanisms of the thirteenth century introduced are maintained with increasing strictness by their modern prototypes, still the regulators of industrialism.

A N INTERESTING process of great commercial importance, though little known to the public, is metalizing.
Defined, it is a method of applying a metallic coating of
any desired thickness on to another material by the use of force
and heat. In its earliest form, patented in 1882, it was a German
process for spraying a stream of molten lead by compressed air.

Since 1910 the art of metalizing has been developed to a high
degree especially in the United States. The spray gun has an air
turbine connected to feed rolls which automatically draw the
wire within and automatically feed it at a constant rate of speed to
the oxyacetylene nozzle. At this point the metal melts into a fine
spray and is blown by compressed air against the surface to be
coated. Since the bond is purely mechanical and no fusion or
weld takes place, no flux, acid, or preheating is needed. The melted
wire, emerging in a luminous spray, is fascinating to watch.

To list all of the uses to which this process has been put would
require several pages. Most important of them are building up
worn parts of machinery, coating rapidly-oxidizing metals with
slower-oxidizing surfaces, coating the inside of vats in chemical
industries, decorating architectural structures, and repairing de-
fective castings.

Courtesy
John A. Maloney

METALIZING; "SPRAYING" A PART WITH MOLTEN METAL

BECAUSE the joining of two or more pieces of metal together by means of welding requires highly concentrated forms of energy, it was not until the nineteenth century, when such energy became available to man, that the process of welding as we know it came into use. There are three fundamental methods by which such energy can now be obtained and these are known as oxyacetylene welding, electric welding and thermite welding.

The oxyacetylene method of welding makes use of the intense heat that is generated when oxygen and acetylene are mixed and burned in proper proportions. Welding rods, coated with chemicals to prevent oxidation, are held at the point of the flame, where their surfaces are rapidly blended together, making a bond that is stronger than the metals themselves. If such a welded joint is placed in a testing machine and tested to its ultimate destruction the break will usually occur in the pieces joined rather than at the welded joint. The oxyacetylene torch which is used in welding is also a very efficient tool for cutting through metals quickly and neatly.

In 1886 Elihu Thomson invented the welding process which bears his name. Using low voltage and high amperage electrical currents, he found that pieces of metal held together mechanically could be easily welded if the current was passed along the joint. The tremendous heat thus generated in the metal caused them to fuse. This process has since been applied widely to large-scale welding operations.

Another form of electric welding is called spot welding. In this process, two copper electrodes make instantaneous contact with the two pieces of metal and pass a current through them which welds them together at that one point.

In 1894 C. Vautin found that when aluminum in a powdered state is mixed with metallic oxides and ignited, the chemical reaction caused a temperature as high as 3,000° C. He did not apply his discovery commercially and it was left for Dr. Johann Goldschmidt to make a successful commercial procedure of the

Courtesy International Harvester Co.

ELECTRIC WELDING IN A TRACTOR MANUFACTURING PLANT

Courtesy Allis-Chalmers Mfg. Co.

WELDING A STATOR FOR A GIGANTIC GENERATOR

phenomenon. The thermite process has been used successfully for welding railroad rails and steel girders, and in the manufacture of various types of steel.

The thermite process can also be reversed. For example, when the girders which supported the towers of the Sky-Ride at the recent Century of Progress in Chicago were being dismantled, the effectiveness of thermite was shown. The base of one girder was surrounded by a container of aluminum and iron oxide. When this was ignited the base of the steel girder melted as if it were butter. The same operation done with hack saws would have required several days. With thermite it was a matter of minutes.

AFTER Eli Whitney lost hope for profits from his invention of the cotton gin, he returned to his native New England, and at New Haven, Connecticut, began the manufacture of firearms. His inventive and organizing genius enabled him to design successfully machine tools and put into practice, for the first time in history, the principle of standardized, interchangeable parts. His profits were large, but the gain of the world as a result of making this system practical is truly immeasurable.

Modern industry, in fact modern society, could not exist without making use of Whitney's system. Articles from pins to automobiles could not be manufactured in large quantities. Nor could the cost be kept low. Repairs would be most expensive, and never could be made expediently.

When Whitney received the contract from the government in 1798 to manufacture ten thousand stands of arms, to be delivered in two years, he found that guns, like all other articles, were built rather than manufactured. That is, each gun was individually made. Following a model, using only hand tools, no two guns were made alike. Each part was designed to fit only one gun. If a trigger broke, repair consisted of making a trigger to fit the individual gun. A trigger from another gun would not fit.

Whitney determined to make a model musket and copy it precisely. Each part must fit any and all muskets. He introduced and designed three aids: drilling by pattern, filing by guides, and milling of irregular forms. He failed to manufacture a single musket for two years. Instead, he designed machines and tools. English and French military officers who visited his plant laughed at his system. The government began to worry about Whitney's ability to fulfill his contract.

Then, one day, the inventor appeared in the office of the Secretary of War with a load of parts. Separating them into piles, each containing ten units of the same segment of a gun and taking one from each pile at random, he put together a musket, with each part fitting exactly. Ten such guns were fitted together. After machines were designed that would cut parts precisely to models, it made little difference how many guns were ordered. By making standard, interchangeable parts, and by dividing labor into small units, the manufacturer found that no order would be too large. Soon contracts for firearms were pouring into Whitneyville.

One illustration of the type of machine tools invented by Whitney is the jig, now used in wood-working, metal-working and manufacturing shops throughout the world. This machine tool with an insignificant name is a box, in which is placed the object to be worked upon. The pattern forms the cover of the box. If six holes, for example, are to be drilled into a plate in certain positions so as to match the holes in a counterpart, the pattern is made with the holes correctly located. The plates are then put into the box, and the drill is placed through each hole in the pattern cover. Each successive plate introduced will have holes cut in the exact places. They will be identical.

This "American System," as the standardization of parts was called, has revolutionized industry. The great industries of today —the automobile, farm machinery, in fact, the very necessities of life—are possible only by the use of the system introduced by Whitney. Quantity production at low cost, making possible the wide distribution of luxuries and raising the standard of living, has been the result.

FINER THAN SPLIT HAIR

Standardization of parts became almost universal in the industrial world by the twentieth century. By that time, however, a new problem had been created. As machines became more complex there was need for greater mechanical exactitude in order to make various units absolutely identical.

This need gave rise to the precision machinery in use today. So close are measurements made that parts are manufactured within a quarter of one ten-thousandth of an inch. Such a figure

A STEEL-BORING MACHINE

This huge device uses the principles on which Eli Whitney started the use of standardized parts. The many drills show its variety of operations.

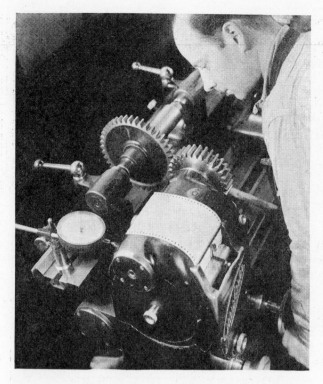

ACCURACY PLUS
A gear-testing device which shows, on dial and chart, infinitesimal variations from the master gear or pattern.

Courtesy International Harvester Co.

is almost incomprehensible. A single hair, split into ten equal parts, would still be ten times too thick for precision manufacturing. The one-tenth of a single hair has to be divided into ten equal parts before a measurement as small as that necessary to meet approval in modern industry is attained. Gauges, so exactly machined that they adhere by molecular attraction, are in general use today.

Such close measuring permits perfect fittings to be made, and reduces wear. Today it is possible for an autoist whose fuel pump is out of order to insert a new part that fits to within a fraction of a thousandth of an inch. When we recall that Watt had to be satisfied with a piston roughly fitting the cylinder of his steam engine, we realize how far precision in manufacturing has come.

ORE THAN TWO-THIRDS of the surface of the
earth is locked under the jealous waters of oceans, seas,
and lakes: a whole separate world of mystery, airless
save for the oxygen and nitrogen dissolved in the water itself and in complete darkness save for the eerie phosphorescence
of certain fish and plants. This world has mountains whose peaks
are the rocks that sailors fear, and valleys deep enough to swallow
the Himalayas. There are whole classes of animal and vegetable
life which have adapted themselves to the great undersea pressures.
There may even be the ruins of man-built cities there; but in any
case there are ships, sunken ships of all ages: Phoenician traders,
Chinese junks, Roman triremes, Viking dragon-boats, Spanish
galleons, clippers, steamships, battleships and submarines, some of
them freighted with the precious metal that has always given an
added zest to man's unceasing interest in picking Davy Jones's
locker—gold.

The earliest divers had no more equipment than a heavy stone
to speed them to the bottom. The ancient pearl-fishers of Ceylon
tied this weight to a cord, which guided and aided them in as-
cending, and by which they could send up their basket of oysters.
Armed with an ironwood sword against dangerous fish, they could
reach a depth of more than thirty feet and stay under for more
than a minute. However, they were limited to the amount of
air that their lungs alone could hold. At a date too early for
historical record some divers began to use hollow reeds to breathe
through, or tubes of leather attached at the surface to a small
float or bladder. This was dangerous at best and very tiring, since
the lungs forcibly had to suck the air down against the pressure
of the water. However, the divers of Alexander the Great, who
were reputed to have destroyed the submarine fortifications of
besieged Tyre, may have employed such a method. It offered an
obvious advantage to spies, by enabling them to remain indefinitely a little way under water, unseen and unsuspected.

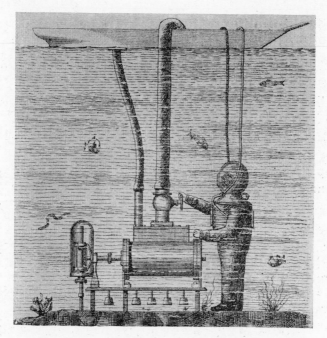

EARLY DIVING
SUIT AND SUB-
MARINE ROCK
DRILL

DOWN TO THE SEA IN BELLS

During equally early times the diving-bell came into use. The
diving-bell makes use of a very simple principle. If an empty,
upended glass be pushed down into water, it does not fill; the pressure of the air in it keeps out the water. As the glass goes
down deeper and deeper, the air is compressed into a smaller and
smaller volume. However, this is a relatively slow process; a depth
of thirty-three feet is reached before the water fills half the container. Such a bell, constructed of metal or watertight wood,
could be large enough to contain several men or small enough to
be worn like a helmet. It could be weighted in such a way as to
lessen the danger of upsets. Alexander the Great himself is said
to have gone under water in one. However, there seemed at first
no way to replenish the air in such a bell when it became foul from
breathing. An open tube leading to the surface obviously could
not be used; it would liberate the compressed air, and water
would instantly fill the bell. In 1717, Edmund Halley described

a method for sinking supplies of fresh air down in weighted barrels that went up and down like elevators. This method was more ingenious than practical; furthermore, it was of little help in alleviating the foulness of the accumulated air, which it diluted rather than changed.

Nevertheless, the lure of treasure in shallow waters was so great that men kept risking their lives in helmets and other devices, sometimes wearing semi-waterproof leather clothes and sometimes not. From ancient days until the beginning of the last century, styles in diving costume and equipment changed many times, but the main principles remained essentially the same. No further progress was possible until the use of the air-force-pump was introduced. Augustus Siebe made this innovation in 1819, when he invented his "open" diving dress. It consisted of a bell-shaped helmet connected by a tube with an air pump at the surface. The pump replenished the air and maintained sufficient pressure to keep the water below the diver's chin; surplus air escaped under the edge of the helmet.

Courtesy Museum of Science and Industry, Chicago

UNDERWATER METAL CUTTING
As demonstrated at the Museum of Science and Industry, Chicago.

This arrangment was obviously very precarious. If the diver stumbled and fell while prowling about the murky bottom, his helmet would immediately fill with water and he would drown if not hoisted quickly to the surface; if the pump happened to lose pressure for any reason, the same thing would happen. In 1830 Siebe made his diving suit watertight. The metal helmet was attached to a suit made of waterproof leather. Moreover, the helmet was provided with a cunning valve that let used air escape without letting water in. The diver, by regulating this valve, could lessen or increase the amount of air in his suit. Thus he could vary his buoyancy while working on the ocean bottom, seeing to it that he was neither too heavy to move easily nor too light to keep his footing and balance. In emergencies he could close the valve, puff his suit out with air, and "blow" himself to the surface.

WHAT THE MODERN DIVER WEARS

Despite many small improvements, most modern diving suits are essentially similar to the one invented by Siebe. They protect the diver from the water, but not from the pressure of the water. As he goes down the air he draws into his lungs is compressed more and more. As a result, more nitrogen and oxygen are dissolved in his blood. If he is then drawn too swiftly to the surface, the pressure too quickly withdrawn, his blood behaves like the carbonated water in a bottle from which the cap has been removed. Small bubbles of nitrogen form in the blood stream, giving rise to the dangerous caisson disease or "bends." If the diver is drawn slowly to the surface, there is sufficient time for the gas to dissipate without forming bubbles. Today attempts are being made to use, instead of nitrogen, helium, an inert gas that does not dissolve readily. Employing this method in December 1937, Max Nohl of Milwaukee descended 420 feet into Lake Michigan, breaking all previous records.

However, in any case the body of a diver can stand only so much direct pressure. The divers who salvaged the U. S. A. submarine "F-4" in 27 feet of water went to about the greatest depth at which much useful work can be accomplished in a dress of the Siebe pattern. Today all-metal diving suits, that may attain

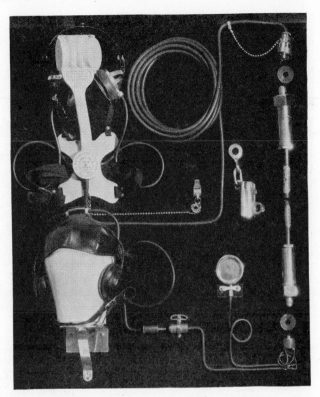

BATTERYLESS
TELEPHONE
EQUIPMENT FOR
UNDERWATER
USE

Courtesy Museum of
Science and Industry,
Chicago

even better results, have been invented by Neufeldt and Kuhnke;
a steel and aluminum alloy withstands the force of water and allows the diver inside to breathe air at normal pressure. These suits
look like massive, many-jointed robots. The hands of the diver
do not protrude; each metallic arm ends in a hook or pair of tongs
that can be manipulated from within. Similar in principle is Dr.
William Beebe's bathysphere, a strong thick metal globe capable
of withstanding the prodigious pressures that accumulate at a
depth of three thousand feet, and fitted for scientific observation
with six-inch windows of fused quartz.

Today the diver, working usually in the old-style flexible suit,
is the key man in any attempts to raise sunken ships or to pick
Davy Jones's locker directly. Communicating with the salvage
boat above by means of a telephone or a code of jerks on a rope,
he acts as an invaluable advance guard. With the aid of an in-

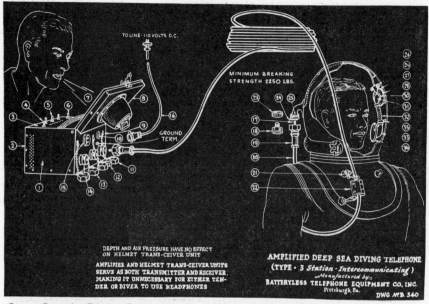

Courtesy Batteryless Telephone Equipment Co., Inc.

LIST OF PARTS OF THE AMPLIFIED DEEP SEA DIVING TELEPHONE

(1) Amplifier Unit Assembly; (2) Case Assembly; (3) Front Panel Assembly; (4) Operator's Key;
(5) Station Key; (6) Main Switch; (7) Trans-ceiver Unit; (8) Cover Assembly (9) Rear Panel
Assembly; (10) Supervisor's Jack Box; (11) Jack Box Cover with Ball Chain; (12)
Supervisor's Jack Box Cover with Chain; (13) Power Receptacle Cover with Chain;
(14) Station Jack Box; (15) Power Receptacle; (16) Power Cable Assembly;
(17) Jack Plug; (18) Protecting Cap; (19) Jack Plug Housing; (20) Combination Telephone & Life Line Cable; (21) Quickly-Detachable Safety
Clasp; (22) Cable Safety Clamp; (23) Protecting Cap Nut; (24)
Leather Washer; (25) Gooseneck Jack Box; (26) Leader Cord;
(27) Trans-ceiver Case; (28) Trans-ceiver Unit; (29) Ad-
justable Retainer Clamp; (30) L-Fitting Clamp Ring;
(31) L-Fitting; (32) Flexible Tube; (33) Mouthpiece; (34) Rubber Mouthpiece Protector
Ring; (35) Mouthpiece Clamp.

candescent lamp designed to shine under water, he determines
the general position of the sunken ship and the amount of damage
it has sustained. With this information at hand, it is decided what
is the best scheme of salvaging. Cables may be slipped under
the wreck and attached at low tide to empty hulks, and the rising
tide allowed to lift the ship high enough to tow under water. In
this case the diver may have to guide a hydraulic, high-pressure
borer to make space for the cables between the ship and the bottom. Or the damage may be so slight that the wreck can be
pumped full of air and floated after a few minor repairs. In this
case the diver himself will make the repairs, sometimes using an

oxyelectric torch whose cutting and welding flame is enclosed by a ring-shaped jet of compressed air. Afterwards he may help to introduce the buoyant air into the ship by operating an electric submersible pump, which is not hermetically sealed but instead has most of its working parts exposed.

Perhaps the wreck cannot readily or possibly be raised. Then divers must do the whole job, exploring the interior of the ship, cutting through walls and safes to get at valuable cargo. In this fashion five million pounds' worth of bullion was recovered from the *Laurentic*, lying one hundred and twenty feet below the surface, her plates and decks all crumpled after a storm. During such explorations the air tube is even more inconvenient than usual and more liable to the danger of breaking. Toward the end of the last century H. A. Fleuss designed a suit that did not need a tube. The diver carried a cylinder of oxygen and air strapped to his chest, a chamber containing caustic soda to purify the breathed air strapped to his back. Using such an apparatus a diver, in 1882, went through a quarter of a mile of completely flooded tunnel to close a sluice valve and an iron gate. This man's short trip, during which, unlinked by tube or cord to his fellow workers, with no surface above him to strive after if things went wrong, he had to fight obstacles as well as water, is poignantly illustrative of the terrors and marvels of modern diving.

THE FUTURE OF DEEP-SEA DIVING

In the future we shall undoubtedly see salvagers and scientists working at consistently greater depths in all-metal suits and bathyspheres. And in the shallower parts of oceans and lakes, more and more students and amateurs will be exploring the mysteries of undersea life, using open helmets and simple pumps. With a little ingenuity these men will be able to do many things in the lesser depths—things that one usually thinks of as limited to land life. Notes can be taken under the water by writing with a stylus on a wax tablet; undersea gardens can be tended and studied; fish hunted with bow and metal arrows—wooden ones would rise to the surface—or accustomed to the diver's presence and so studied. Since both oil and oil paints repel water, pictures in color might even be made upon waterproof canvas!

SEEING THE UNSEEN

THE history of the motion picture projector and camera and the history of the stroboscope have much in common. Both of them began as amusing toys, both make use of the persistence of vision of the human eye, and both have become important tools of science and industry. Through the medium of the ultra-slow motion picture we are able to bring rapidly moving objects into clear focus and to study details which would otherwise remain hidden forever from prying eyes. With the stroboscope we can do the same thing. In fact the latest method of taking slow motion pictures in industrial and scientific laboratories uses both the movie camera and the stroboscope at the same time. Instead of using a shutter which opens and closes in front of the moving film, the film is whirled through the camera and the picture is taken by the light of the stroboscope.

THE EDGERTON STROBOSCOPE
This device is used as a light source in the photographing of rapidly moving mechanisms.

The stroboscope is simply a rapidly flashing light which can be controlled to move in synchronization with any swiftly moving object. Let us suppose that we are having difficulty with an automobile engine valve—trouble that occurs only when the engine is running at high speeds. With the unaided eye we can see nothing but a blur as the valve opens and closes hundreds of times a minute. Flash the light, usually neon or mercury, on the valve at the same rate as the valve is operating, and it appears to stand still. So clearly does the valve now appear that the trouble is immediately evident. Multiply the engine valve by millions of other devices that move at high speeds and you have some idea of the vast application of this simple but ingenious device, the stroboscope. Its name, which is taken from the Greek language, means to look at a whirling object.

By using the slow-motion camera and the stroboscope it is possible to see exactly what happens when an electric light bulb breaks, when a golf ball leaves the surface of an iron, when a drop of water falls. In this way it is possible to read secrets of nature which can be discovered in no other way.

THE discovery of glass is one that takes us back to the period before history was written. But although we may follow the progress of the industry up through the ages, we arrive at the twentieth century before we come upon startling new uses for glass. It was the development of thin, transparent plastic films by the chemical industry that pointed the way to the first great improvement—safety or shatterproof glass. The first attempts to make this type of glass for automobiles met with failure because the product became discolored after a few months of use. But it was soon found that if the edges of the glass were sealed so that no air or moisture could get between the sandwiched glass sheets which held the plastic, such glass would last indefinitely.

When an object strikes this type of glass the plastic film holds the pieces of broken glass together. Since shatterproof glass is universally used in automobile windows and windshields it can readily be imagined how many lives have been saved through its use.

Courtesy Buffalo Museum of Science, Buffalo, N. Y.

PRIMITIVE MANUFACTURE OF GLASS

SAFETY (NON-SHATTERABLE) GLASS IN AUTOMOBILES
A streetcar hit this auto, but no broken glass endangered the passengers.

CELLULOSE ACETATE PLASTIC HOLDS BROKEN PIECES OF GLASS
IN PLACE, PREVENTING FRAGMENTS FROM FLYING

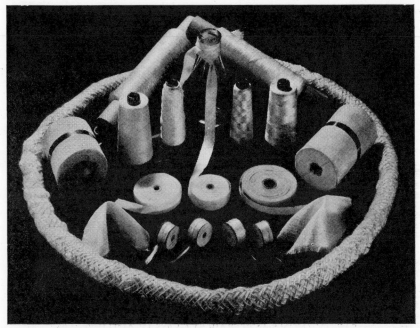

ALL MADE OF GLASS

Textile glass used for insulating purposes assumes many shapes and forms. Glass
"yarn" can now be woven or braided into any form.

Quickly upon the heels of the discovery of safety glass came
the development of flexible glass. This glass is manufactured in
the same way as plate glass, but the final step in finishing it consists in cooling it very rapidly. This rapid cooling imparts a tough
film to the entire outer surface of such glass, and it can then be
bent to a much greater degree than can ordinary plate glass. It can
not, however, be cut or ground after it is made. The reason for
this is that its interior is under such stress that if its surface is
punctured, the glass flies into billions of particles smaller than
pin-heads.

The third important innovation in the modern glass industry
is the recent perfection of a process for spinning glass into a strong
and efficient thread and weaving it into articles that range all the
way from milady's evening dress to laboratory filters for the
chemical industry. If you heat a piece of glass to incandescence,

touch a glass rod to it, and pull the rod away with a rapid and even motion, you will secure a fine glass thread. In making such thread commercially, a machine is used, and the glass is treated chemically to eliminate the brittleness of ordinary glass. The thread comes from the machine at an incredible speed and is woven into cloth on regular textile machinery.

Courtesy Corning Glass Works

GLASS BLOWER SHAPING A RETORT
Most glassware is blown in molds, but some pieces must still be blown "off hand," calling for a high degree of skill.

MICROSCOPIC FENCES

VISIBLE light can have many mysterious qualities, but none more mysterious than that of polarization.

Imagine a microscopic picket fence with pickets so narrow and close together that only up-and-down vibrations of light could get through it. Such light would be polarized. If it met another microscopic fence with the pickets set at the same angle as the first, it could pass through, but if they were set at right angles, it could not. The up-and-down vibrations could not get through the crosswise openings. The beam of light would be cut off short.

Since the end of the seventeenth century it has been known that certain mineral crystals, among them Iceland spar, polarize light. But they are rare, and are seldom found except as small fragments. Nevertheless, they have had a limited scientific use. Recently, Edwin H. Land, by treating quinine sulphate with iodine, invented an organic material called herapathite. The individual herapathite crystals polarized light but were microscopic in size. Land embedded them in a plastic film, stretched the film to make the crystals lie parallel, as if in rows of pickets, and sandwiched the film tightly between two plates of glass. He called the final product polaroid. It can be made in any size.

Courtesy The Polaroid Corporation

THE EFFECT OF POLAROID
View at left shows a scene as it appears through ordinary anti-glare lenses, and at the right through polaroid lenses.

THE PERILS OF NIGHT DRIVING
Approaching headlights as they usually appear.

NIGHT DRIVING MADE SAFER
The same headlights as they look through a polaroid visor

Courtesy The Polaroid Corporation

Courtesy The Polaroid Corporation

ORDINARY ILLUMINATION
Page obscured by glare.

POLAROID ILLUMINATION
The glare is removed.

This new substance may bring polarized light into general commercial use, with startling results. For example, if two panes of ordinary glass were placed in our line of vision, we could see through them as easily as if there were only one. But if those panes were polaroid it would be possible to place them at such an angle that they would make a background blacker than night; at another angle, and they would look like ordinary glass. Again, if automobile headlights sent out only light polarized vertically, and if windshields let through only light polarized horizontally, then the problem of night glare would be solved; the driver would see everything except the headlights of the other cars. Polaroid might be employed for interior illumination, especially in art galleries and workshops, where glare and blurring are most objectionable. Used in sun glasses, it cuts down the amount of light transmitted, without changing the colors.

However, these uses of polaroid may not have such far reaching consequences as its ability to spy out weak spots in transparent materials.

INVISIBLE ENEMIES

There is an invisible, omnipresent danger of weak areas in all engineering products and building construction, in all machinery, and in all things machine-made and hand-made. The weak spot does not reveal itself until a bridge falls, a skyscraper collapses, a dirigible crumples, or a hard rubber comb snaps in two. When a bar of iron is bent, there is a visible deformation; that is called strain. But there is also an inner tension; the molecules are pulling at one another, attempting to shear apart; that is the invisible danger called stress.

It is impossible to know beforehand just where the greatest load will appear in a steel girder or machine part. Computations based on the theory of elasticity are not only very difficult to make; they cannot be solved precisely for shapes of any complexity. Rule of thumb methods tend to allow too great a factor of safety in some places, too little in others. Stress constitutes a very difficult problem.

But there is a way of spying out the invisible danger directly, a way that may eventually give great assistance to engineers. It depends upon polarized light. Imagine two plates of polaroid set up a little way apart and at such angles that light could pass through them. Then suppose there was placed between them a transparent substance that twisted or rotated the polarized light through a certain angle. Then the second fence would have to be set at that same certain angle to transmit any light.

In 1816 the British physicist Brewster discovered that invisible stresses in plate glass will rotate polarized light. If any such transparent material is viewed between two polarizers, the stresses will be seen as a pattern of curving bands of light. These bands may radiate out from the point at which pressure is being applied to the material, they may cluster around screw holes, or concentrate at edges and corners—everywhere pointing out the weak spots, the spots where dangerous stresses accumulate. What is learned from transparent materials, such as glass and various plastics, can be applied to opaque materials such as steel, providing only that the greater strength of the latter be taken into consideration. Flaws invisible to the eye or X-ray thus yield their secret to polarized light.

INVENTIVE URGES LEAD TO THE creation of strange and weird devices, some useful, some merely entertaining, and some completely worthless. Millions of people have dreamed of becoming inventors, and judging from the number of contraptions that flood the market most of them have succeeded. There is a wide field in which ingenuity runs wild, devising and making appliances, accessories, and independent units. Some of these inventions, popularly called "gadgets," eventually win a respectability which can be explained only by their genuine usefulness and the alacrity with which people accept novel combinations.

A gadget may be defined as an ingenious device used for economy of time or labor, convenience, or just plain fun, innocent or otherwise. Many well-established inventions began as mere gadgets, interesting but apparently worthless. Hero's steam engine used one of the principles now employed in giant turbines. The magnet is indispensable in electrical generators and wherever magnetism is used. Both originally were gadgets. The automobile has offered an almost unparalleled opportunity for gadget makers to tempt motorists.

The vast majority of gadgets, facetiously called doodads, rigamajigs, thingamies, thingabobs, or almost anything else, quickly return to the oblivion from which they were conjured. The survivors are everywhere—in homes, offices, and factories; in pockets, on desks, around arms, necks, and legs; hidden in machines or clothing. Inventions almost without number literally flood the market, playing an important role in business, industry, and the home. Any classification of gadgets is certain to be more or less an arbitrary arrangement, and there are many of these interesting "doodads" that defy orderly grouping.

Automobile owners have a peculiar weakness for accessories. The first machines were little more than a combination of chassis, motor, and seats. The gadget makers entered the market gleefully, tempting the motorist with a bewildering array of appliances. The klaxon, more prosaically called the horn, began as a large rubber bulb attached to the end of a trumpet. One squeezed the bulb, forcing air over vibrators that emitted a raucous squawk. Then came the push horns, with a geared or notched plunger that activated the vibrators. The next step was to make a small electric motor which was fastened to one end of the horn. A touch of the button on the wheel or steering-rod casing closed a circuit that started the little motor. Musical notes operating from the exhaust sound two or more notes. Perhaps the latest refinement in warning signals was patented late in 1937. Combinations of admonitory words are recorded on a disc which may be played at the motorist's pleasure. So it is that the automobile has been made to speak, and the unwary pedestrian may be startled to hear a loud "Look out!" shouted by an approaching car. Bumpers, snubbers, radiator ornaments, heaters, windshield wipers, windshield fans, electric cigar lighters, and radios are a few of the accessories which have become so common that the term gadget may no longer be properly applied to them.

AN ELECTRIC
SHAVING DEVICE

Courtesy Progress
Corporation, Chicago

THY NAME IS BUT VANITY

Many years ago, long before the Christian Era, women turned to artificial means of improving the beauty of their countenances. The savage used a crude paint pot; the Egyptian had a vanity case. Made of brass, silver, gold, or platinum, plain or exquisitely wrought with precious gems, the vanity case has become a compact. A mirror inside of the cover, a miniature powder puff, and a rouge dauber are almost indispensable. The powder which rescues shiny noses, chins, and cheeks from glaring prominence may be in a lens-shaped cake, or loose in a little compartment closed by a lid fastened to a spring. Lipsticks, in various shades of red and even flavored, are important adjuncts to the portable beauty shop, without which a woman usually feels very uncomfortable. These beauty aids are enclosed in telescoping tubes, or attached to tiny pistons.

The curling iron, once a rather clumsy affair with wooden handles which was heated over a flame, has become an electrical appliance, and imparts wondrous waves to unruly hair. Millions of dollars are paid annually to "beauty culturists" who periodically attach a profusion of finger-like irons to the hair of women who seek an elusive pulchritude. The result is rather mistakenly called a "permanent" wave. Gadgets they are, but of significant economic importance.

The old, straight-edged razor may still hold its honored place in barber shops. In the hands of the adolescent or nervous man, the barber's razor becomes a dangerous, almost lethal, weapon. So a safety razor was invented, with a short blade that was protected by a guard. Various types of safety razors flood the market. Some are very simple in construction, consisting of a short handle and holder in which the blade is held by a snap cover. Another carries narrow blades in the handle, from which they are ingeniously ejected into the holder, at the same time pushing out the dull blade. Now electric razors, supposed to last indefinitely, threaten to make serious inroads on the lucrative safety razor business. Shavers, like automobile owners, have been particularly vulnerable to sharpening devices. One razor strops itself—with considerable assistance. Abrasive grinders enclosed in a handy case have found many buyers.

SAFETY DEVICES

A number of gadgets have won wide popularity in clothing. The ancient hook-and-eye, and its more recent relative, the snap fastener, has been universally adopted; nor should one forget the lowly and multitudinous family of "ordinary" and safety pins. A few years ago, an inventor with compassion for unmarried men emancipated his brothers from the tyranny of thimble, needle, thread, and broken buttons. This unsung hero made a metal bachelor button in two parts. The lower part has a little rivet-like head which is inserted into an opening in the underside of the top piece. The channel has minute fingers, or springs controlled from a small, movable disc. When nails, wire, or twine fail to serve as satisfactory substitutes, the bachelor button finds favor with the wearer of overalls.

A large industry has developed during the post-war period that has already made significant inroads on the different kinds of fasteners. This new device is popularly known as the "zipper." At first merely a neat gadget, the zipper has found acceptance on galoshes, sweaters, coats, trousers, dresses, and even hats. A Parisian designer in 1937 made a complete outfit of feminine clothing without the use of even one button. Brief cases, tobacco pouches, key rings, purses—all have succumbed to the speedy and accurate zipper. This device is so simple that the user wonders why he did not think of it himself. Two rows of little teeth or lugs, fixed on strips of fabric, are made to interlock by sliding a V-shaped guide. So popular has this gadget become that factories have difficulty in filling orders.

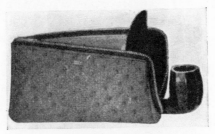

Courtesy Iwan Ries & Co.
THE "ZIPPER" APPLIED ON A
TOBACCO POUCH

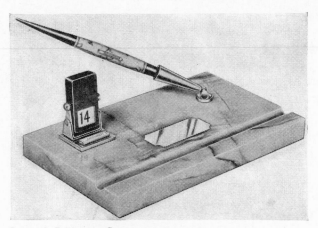

Courtesy L. E. Waterman Co

CALENDAR-AND-PEN DESK SET

WRITING GADGETS

Ever since the stylus was first invented to write on clay tablets inventors have been developing sundry gadgets for writing. The fountain pen, originally, was simply a pen with an inkwell attachment. From this crude beginning refinements were made—the size of the well was made smaller and less cumbersome, the ink was made to flow more evenly, and the nibs were improved. The most radical advance was made when a rubber sack was inserted which could be filled by means of a lever, thus doing away with the messy job of filling. Recently, because rubber was subject to deterioration, a sackless pen was put on the market which works on the vacuum theory by means of a pump at the end of the pen which, when pulled out, creates the vacuum which sucks in the ink. Another deviation uses a hollow stylus instead of the regulation nib which is supposed to make for smoother writing.

Similarly, in the field of the automatic pencil, various gadgets have found ready sale. The earliest form was merely a tube in which a pencil-tipped inner tube moved up and down at the turn of a knob at the end. The latest gadget is able to write in a number of different colors. This same idea has been recently adapted to the ordinary pencil which uses a cluster of five different colored leads imbedded in its center which writes red or blue or yellow at a turn of the pencil. Another writing gadget is the "magic pad" which is a blue-wax-coated cardboard covered with a sheet of opaque celluloid. When an impression is made on the celluloid with any sharp point, the colored wax adheres to the various points of contact which show through the celluloid. By simply lifting the celluloid from the wax, the impression disappears and the pad is ready for another notation.

SHADES OF SIR WALTER RALEIGH

Tobacco-smoking has brought with it an avalanche of gadgets. A thousand different pipes with a thousand different methods of straining the smoke, cooling it, and sweetening it have been perfected. Pipe-cleaners, replaceable pipe bowls, wind-proof pipes, pipe-scrapers, pipe-drainers, pipe-racks, moisture-proof pipe bits —all of these have appeared and disappeared in the pipe-smoker's market. Cigarette gadgets have outnumbered those for pipes. The

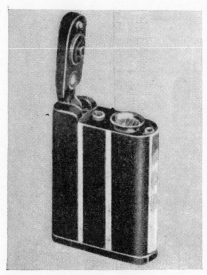

Courtesy Iwan Ries & Co.
CIGARETTE LIGHTER

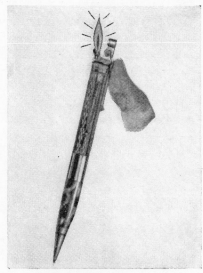

COMBINATION PENCIL AND
LIGHTER

first, perhaps, was the cigarette, itself, which was considered at first effeminate, foppish, and therefore transitory. Following came metal troughs and wooden rods for making cigarettes at home; cigarettes with a paper tube at the end for a shorter and cleaner smoke; cigarette holders both long and short, some devised to purify the smoke, others with spring attachments to eject the unsmoked butt remaining. The most recent has a stem in which a second cigarette, other than the one being smoked, is placed, the purpose of which is to strain out the nicotine and moisture.

For smokers, too, there have been invented innumerable devices for lighting their favorite smoke. The earlier lighters were outgrowths of the primitive flint and steel method of obtaining a spark, which ignited a piece of cord that was impregnated with an inflammable fluid. One of these lighters used a globule of a chemical compound which, when exposed to air, ignited. The very latest lighter uses only a chemical fluid, the fumes of which, when sucked through a platinum wire grid, cause the metal to glow, igniting the cigarette. Recently, a cigarette case was invented which, at the push of a button, ejected a lighted cigarette. Gadget cigarette containers and cases have appeared ever since the cigarette became a popular smoke. The most ingenious have tiny figures on them which bend over, pick out a cigarette and proffer it to the smoker.

VARIOUS OTHER GADGETS

Every kitchen is a repository of gadgets, both useless and useful. Both the ordinary, old-fashioned can opener and the modern hand-cranked opener are nothing more than gadgets. The knife-sharpener, made of two rows of steel discs which form an aperture through which the knife is drawn, is in most kitchens. Corkscrews, coffee percolators, electric toasters, and a variety of other kitchen utensils fall into the same category. Particularly is this so with the combination set of vegetable shredders being sold by street-hawkers. One of these ingenious devices gouges spiral chunks out of potatoes, carrots, and beets which are screwed together and then into a potato. When baked and cut open, the result is both tasty and colorful.

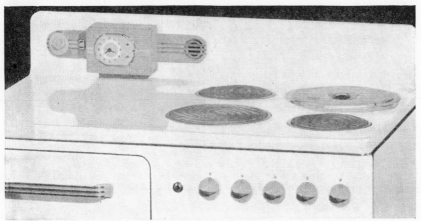

Courtesy Commonwealth Edison Co.
ELECTRIC RANGES GO MODERN THROUGH THE WORK OF
THE "GADGET" MAKERS

Courtesy Commonwealth Edison Co.
THE SILEX COFFEE MAKER

MORE RANGE GADGETS THAT MAKE THE COOKING UNIT
AN ATTRACTIVE PIECE OF FURNITURE

THE GADGET MAN HAS BEEN WORKING ON THE
ELECTRIC REFRIGERATOR, TOO!

Mechanical tools are, in the main, gadgets. The combination knife with its blades of scissors, screwdriver, bottle-opener, corkscrew, pliers, nippers, saw, file, and even a knife blade, is the supreme "doo-jigger" in this field. Another combination tool has its component parts secreted in the handle. The hammer with a magnetized head to pick up and hold tacks is another example.

Gadgets have found their way into business offices in great numbers. The first mechanical method of clipping papers together was accomplished by a gadget that automatically cut a tongue and slit in the papers and slipped the tongue into the slit. The latest development is a wire stapler that inserts a wire staple into a sheaf of papers and bends over the ends. Other office devices include glue-tape sealers, pencil sharpeners, automatic postage-stamp affixers, envelope sealers, envelope slitters, mimeograph machines, addressographs, chemical ink erasers, in fact almost everything to facilitate the quick disposal of office routine.

Restaurants, too, have come in for their share of gadgets. Meat and bread slicing machines, ingenious sugar dispensers that automatically measure out a teaspoon of sugar, patent bottle tops for sauces and other liquid condiments are among them. The sipping straw is nothing more than a gadget, as are the butter cutters—which cut up a butter brick into small patties—napkin holders, and the pie-slice gauges.

Practically all games are gadgets, particularly those which are used for gambling. The pin-ball games are of an intricate nature and are being designed by specialized engineers. The many ingenious slot machines for dispensing gum, peanuts, cigarettes, handkerchiefs, perfume, soft-drinks, and moving pictures are gadgets of the first order. In the field of practical jokes gadgets are supreme. The latest is a key-wound spring which fits into the palm of the hand. When the hand is offered for a handshake the contact causes the spring to unwind itself with a rattle causing the victim to recoil. Other practical jokes are percussion-cap exploders that fit into books, match boxes, cigarette packs, and letters; cigarettes that squirt water when proffered; flowers that spray water when smelled; trick spoons that break in the middle, knives indented to hold peas; forks with lead prongs; and water glasses that allow the liquid contents to dribble over the drinker; spring snakes that

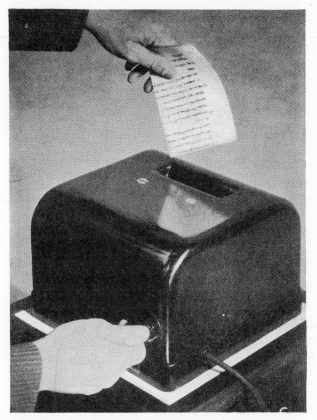

Paul's Photos, Chicago

A PAPER SHREDDING MACHINE
When business men want to be certain a document is
destroyed, they feed it through this device.

pop out of fountain pens, cameras, pickle jars, cold cream tubes,
and cigarette holders; soap that turns the hands black; soap that
does not clean at all; matches that explode, refuse to light, or,
when struck, produce a shower of chemical snow; and the hundreds of puzzles that are made of wire, wood, nails, bolts, rings,
and whatnots.

Of the unclassified gadgets there are mousetraps, flytraps,
roachtraps, and burglar traps; automatic card dealers for bridge
games; flashlights at the ends of pens, on key purses, and in vanity

cases; calendars of all kinds, all of which serve a thousand different dubious needs and duties.

There are occasions when a man—or woman—desires to destroy a piece of paper, completely and forever. Fires are not always available, and tearing by hand does not insure final destruction of incriminating documents. A paper shredder, operated by hand or by electricity, solves the problem. A number of small, sharp teeth arranged on cylinders inside a neat metal box, devour a piece of paper and deposit the shreds in a basket. Not even Sherlock Holmes could reconstruct a document once is has passed through this machine.

There is no end to the multiplicity of gadgets that has flooded the world and will continue to flood it as long as we live in the age of speed. For they are the result of our present urge to get things done in as short a time as possible. If their invention continues apace, man in time will be able to perfect devices that will do everything for him; work for him, feed him (of which the automatic feeder in the last Chaplin movie is a grim omen), put him to sleep at night with music, and wake him up in the morning with chimes. We shudder to conjecture on their manifold possibilities. The low and insignificant gadget may yet turn out to be another Frankenstein monster.